NEW

ECHO THREE ZERO

NEW SAS 4

ECHO THREE ZERO: THE BORNEO MISSIONS

Peter Corrigan

First published in Great Britain 1998
22 Books, Invicta House, Sir Thomas Longley Road,
Rochester, Kent

Copyright © 1998 by 22 Books

A CIP catalogue record for this book
is available from the British Library

ISBN 1 86238 011 2

10 9 8 7 6 5 4 3 2 1

Typeset by Hewer Text Ltd, Edinburgh
Printed in Great Britain by
Clays Ltd, St Ives plc

1

Jungles.

I'd always disliked them, personally. These days it's fashionable to rave on about how they're the lungs of the planet and so on. If they are, they're the filthiest, most stinking set of lungs I've ever encountered. Old Mother Earth must be a sixty-a-day type.

People have these ideas about the jungle from old Johnny Weissmuller movies – that it's this colourful, vibrant place teeming with life, a parrot or a snake on every branch, a leopard lurking behind every tree. Absolute rubbish.

Primary jungle – the real stuff – is as dark and cavernous as a cave. It's like a cathedral at dusk, towering over your head and blocking out the light, the trunks of the trees like the pillars supporting a vast roof. Sometimes, way up there, you can see a chink of light where the sun is shining, in another world it seems, but under the canopy it's a twilight existence.

The ground is mud, pure and simple. Nothing can grow in the shade of the huge trees unless it feeds off them or sends some parasitic vine up their trunks to the sunshine above. If you blunder along in the half-light and chance to knock against a hanging vine or dangling branch, you'll find yourself covered with everything from scorpions to leeches. And if you chance across some *rotan* – which is the stick they used to use to clean out drains back in the UK – you'll find yourself caught by ultra-thin filaments that are as strong as wire and covered with backward-facing hooks. It's also called 'wait-awhile' because once you're caught there's no point in stumbling on – you have to stop and disentangle the damn stuff thread by thread.

Having said that, the primary jungle, *ulu*, is a picnic compared with a couple of other types of environment out in the east. There's good old *belukar*, which is an area where the primary vegetation has been cleared for cultivation and then abandoned, so that you get a riot of secondary growth. More sunshine, yes, but a real rat's arse of bushes, saplings, creepers, vines and grass, all of which combine to form a wall of vegetation through which it's more or less impossible to move quietly. And then there's *ladang*, which is land still under cultivation, bare-arsed as the moon and to be avoided at all costs, since the cost of a comfortable march is liable to be a bullet in the head.

Take a land with each of these environments and then punch up through it a series of knife-edged ridges and mountains, all thickly vegetated, steep as a gable roof. Then, in the hollows of the mountains, let the water collect, so that you have fetid, bottomless swamps where a dip could gain you a nice case of Weil's disease or leptospirosis. Add in a few thousand billion mosquitoes, which swarm in the traveller's eyes, nose and mouth as he gasps his way along, and then every so often let rip with a torrential downpour of warm rain, just to keep things nice and damp – and you have your jungle.

And just to spice it up a little, populate the stinking place with a few thousand angry little men with rifles, all itching to shoot off a few rounds. And then you have Malaya in the fifties, where my first experience of the jungle was almost my last. And you have Borneo, ten years later. Which was many times worse.

March 1954

I was twenty-two years old, a member of D Squadron, the 22nd SAS Regiment, re-formed especially for the Malaya 'Emergency' and commanded by the legendary John Woodhouse. It was then that I was given my first introduction to the jolly old jungle, and you know, I didn't think it half bad.

We were a 'hearts and minds' operation as much as anything else in those days. We'd tab off into the *ulu* and be gone a couple of months. We'd be glorified medical orderlies and cultural attachés to a hundred tiny settlements too small and primitive even to be called villages. We'd get the trust of the headman, butter him up a little, heal a few sick babies, and hey presto, that little scrap of jungle was suddenly friendly, a source of food and information.

I was the language expert; I spoke pretty good Malay, even if it probably was with a Scots accent. I'm from Kyleakin, on the Isle of Skye, and inevitably known as 'Jock' in the Squadron. Private Jock Ross I was, back in '54, full of awe for the men around me who'd fought in Korea or the Second World War, one or two of whom had even been with Stirling in the Western Desert. I was a fast learner, though, and had a gift for languages. Our four-man team had me as the interpreter, Sergeant Jim Reese as leader and demo expert, Chalky White as medic and wisecracker, and Eddie Baker as signaller. We were a close little bunch and we were good at our job – so good, in fact, that the local bad lads decided they were going to put an end to our philanthropy. And they did too.

Maybe it's coming from Skye, but the other lads are convinced I have a sixth sense, an uncanny way of telling when something is not right or something is about to happen. I reckon it's all tosh myself, but men will believe in strange things when they've been two or three months in the jungle, living life as it must have been lived in the Stone Age, except that these cavemen carried SLRs.

In any case, I found myself elevated to the status of lead scout, and was often point man when we were hoofing it through the jungle. Though we didn't hoof it, of course. We moved so quietly we could have heard a mouse fart upwind of us. By that stage we were more or less attuned to the *ulu*, the way of moving, the times to pause, even the different sounds of the insects. We had become animals of a sort, and felt as though we were operating in our own backyard, not some alien environment.

On this particular day we had been told by the headman of one village that there was some form of strange activity going on a few miles south of his patch. So Jimmy Reese decided we'd go and take a peek, and I was on point.

I'll never forget that day, not as long as I live.

It was primary jungle, that area, but a couple of the great trees had died and fallen down, so that there was a clearing of sorts, and vegetation on the jungle floor. And light, of course, amazingly bright when your eyes have become accustomed to the gloom of the rain forest. There was no wind – the trees blocked it out. And not a thing stirred, not a beetle, not a leaf – and most certainly not us. Chalky White was behind me, five yards away, behind him was Reese, and bringing up the rear was Eddie Baker with the Clansman radio.

The clearing was perhaps twenty yards wide, and I had paused behind a curtain of bamboo fronds to suss it out. Ten minutes we'd been there by now, still as statues. I was checking out every bush and branch I could see. The hair was standing up on the back of my neck and the sweat was running down the small of my back in a steady stream. Off in the trees I could hear gibbons hooting mockingly, and a hornbill shrieked way off, but that was normal – it was even a good sign.

No, what had me crouching there with all my senses screwed up tight was the sight of a couple of bamboo lean-tos in the middle of the clearing. Interestingly, they had no roofs. The locals would have made roofs out of palm trees, whereas soldiers would have used their waterproof ponchos. This was a little deserted enemy bivouac I was looking at.

We'd already had a quick look at the place and then hiked off for a whispered conference. Reese had decided we should get in closer and examine the ground – from where I was I could even see the glint of empty tin cans rusting in the sunlight. Messy bastards. The place seemed utterly deserted, but you could never tell, and my nerves were jumping. Something didn't feel right.

So I kept us there immobile for half an hour, just watching and listening – listening is incredibly important in the jungle, almost as important as looking – but there was nothing to see or hear.

Some saplings in the deserted camp had been slashed down with parangs, and they now had new shoots, which meant that this place had been built several months ago at least. I was positive that it had been completely abandoned, and there was absolutely no sign of human life in the vicinity, so eventually I looked back at Chalky and nodded at him, then stepped out from behind the bamboo that had been concealing me.

And all hell broke loose.

The volume of noise that instantly erupted was unbelievable. I saw the ground jump at my feet and out of the vegetation on the other side of the clearing all at once there was a brown face and a rifle barrel. I had the sights on him when something gave me a tremendous thump in the hip and I went down. I was still thinking clearly, though, even in the midst of the terrific roar of gunfire. Some other bugger popped his head up and I gave him a double-tap which put him down again. I was wondering how badly I had been hit, where the other lads were, and everything was rocketing through my head at the fucking speed of light.

My legs were dead and useless and my lightweights were full of warm blood. There was no pain as yet – just a queer kind of light-headedness and detachment that I knew was the onset of shock. I wondered if my spine had been hit, and whether that was me now – a cripple for life – not that it seemed I was going to have much more life in front of me at that moment in time. But then I seemed to remember a voice from long ago – some colour-sergeant or other telling me to *move*. Because if you're hit once and you don't move, then you're going to get hit again.

So I crawled back from the spot where I'd been shot, dragging my legs after me like they were two lumps of rubber. There was still fire going down, but it was petering out. 'Shoot and Scoot' was the Standard Operating Procedure we followed. If you're bumped, then basically, you put down as many rounds as you can and leg it out of there – leaving the wounded behind if you have to. It's a harsh rule, and the lads didn't like it, but it saved casualties. You got out and came back later for those you'd left behind, when you had some back-up. The Regiment would never rest, I knew, until they recovered either me or my corpse, but for the moment I was on my own.

The buggers who'd ambushed us seemed more startled than we were by the whole thing. I glimpsed one fleetingly through the trees and he was legging it at top speed. I raised the SLR but decided to pass on it – it would only give away my position again. Instead I concentrated on crawling back into the thickest clump of bushes I could find. There was a hollow beneath them that a jungle pig had scraped out while looking for roots, and into this I hauled myself. I was totally fucked.

It had suddenly become quiet, and the jungle noises had switched off, as they do when the creatures there hear something that is not of the jungle. I got out my field dressings and morphine ampoules and had a look at myself.

The bullet had entered just in front of my left hip, creating a small wound that was easy to slap a dressing on. But it had gone clear through me, exiting from my right buttock. There was a hole there I could put my fist in, a great yawning gap where three inches of muscle had been blasted out of my body. I was glad I couldn't get a good look at it, and stuffed the hole with another dressing as best I could, then gave myself a shot of morphine.

I didn't know it at the time, but I had been incredibly lucky. The bullet had partly severed the great sciatic nerve, paralysing my left leg, and the destruction of the muscles in my buttock had rendered my other leg useless too. But the spine had not been touched, and nor had any major artery. The blood was welling out of me rather than jetting, which was just as well, since there is no way any kind of tourniquet could have worked down there.

We had had a prearranged RV to meet up if this sort of thing happened – it was about three-quarters of a mile back in the jungle, near a clearing where a chopper could pick us up. I knew there was damn little chance of being found where I was, and besides, I didn't care to remain too near the ambush site in case any of our little communist friends showed up again, perhaps with reinforcements. So I levered myself out of my hidey-hole and began to crawl, noting directions with my wrist compass.

I was in *belukar*, that bloody awful mass of secondary growth which is murder to move

10

through. There was primary jungle close by, but I needed the cover that the vegetation afforded. In fact it wasn't that bad – the wild pigs had carved tunnels through the lower undergrowth, which I laboured through gratefully, though wondering what the hell I would do if I came face to face with one of the hairy beasts in my travels. Worst of all were the leeches, which attached themselves to me in clouds, sliding up off the jungle floor to latch on everywhere. They even slid under the field dressings to suck on my wounds. But there was no point in dwelling on it. I just kept crawling, sometimes only managing three yards before pausing to gasp. I still had my belt order on, and two bottles of clean water which I sipped periodically. I had emergency rations too, but the mere thought of food turned my stomach.

Most importantly, I had a smoke grenade on my belt. These were the days before SARBEs (Surface to Air Rescue Beacons) and it was the only way I would have of signalling to a chopper, short of starting a forest fire.

So I crawled. But it was incredibly slow going, and there were moments when I thought it would be so much easier just to lie there and turn up my toes. I thought of all sorts of things as I hauled myself along. I thought a lot about sex and SAS Selection. I had no family to speak of in those days – just my parents back on Skye – so

I thought too of home, gathering driftwood for the fire and being out in my uncle's boat in the Sound of Sleat. Snow on the Cuillin Mountains. I'd like to be crawling through snow, I thought, and wondered what the chances were of a war in Norway. The morphine was getting to me.

I stopped at last, knackered. I thought I'd made about four or five hundred yards, but I was beat, so I crawled into a hollow beneath a fallen tree, blessing those burrowing pigs again, and lay there as the light faded. Actually, in the jungle the light doesn't fade – it just switches off. One moment I was lying there in the dimness able to see shapes and forms, and the next the darkness seemed to creep up out of the very tree roots and it was pitch-black.

Before it had got dark, though, I'd seen a sight which, in my morphine-induced detachment, intrigued me mightily. There had been flies buzzing round my wounds all afternoon. I lifted off the dressing on the entry wound to have a peek – it had stopped bleeding – and there were the little buggers laying eggs in my flesh which were busy turning into maggots.

I replaced the dressing, feeling a little odd, and was glad when darkness came so that I couldn't see them any more.

*   *   *

It was a strange night. I don't think I slept, though I can't remember being awake and aware for long. I remember a battle of will in the small hours as the first shot of morphine began to wear off and the pain started, like a thin, white-hot wire running through my bowels. I squirmed there for what seemed like bloody hours. I had only one shot left and I was determined to save it for the next day. And I remember how ashamed I was when I finally thought, fuck it, and took the second shot. I was determined that if I ever got back to the Squadron I'd never tell the lads how weak I'd been. It distressed me deeply.

The sun rose at last with the sudden violence of the tropics, and the forest went apeshit again as the day shift started their screeching and howling. I knew that today was my last chance – I wouldn't survive a second night in the jungle. I was much weaker this morning, and it was hard to muster up the strength to start that God-awful crawling again. I found out later that the leeches had drained me of almost more blood than my wounds had. They'd been gorging themselves on me all night, which was why I felt feeble as a kitten.

But I got going all the same. It was like Selection all over again – the awesome tiredness, the thought that you could jack it all in if you wanted to, the knowledge too that it was all up to you and no one else. Looking back now, I can see that Selection really does set you up for this kind of thing. You can recognize the hopeless feeling the moment it arrives, and immediately kick it into touch. You've been there, you've done that, and you know you can move on, turn your back on it.

I estimated I was three or four hundred yards away from the RV with its clearing. I'd been crawling for another four and a half hours, and I was dragging the SLR along as though it was a ball and chain, but I was fucked if I was going to leave it behind, even if there wasn't the strength in my arms to get it into the shoulder.

It was then I heard the chopper. One of our little Whirlwinds, without a doubt. It went off to the north of me – near the RV. I debated pulling the pin on the grenade, but I was almost in primary jungle here, and the trees were too vast, the canopy too thick even for a harness to have been lowered down. Cursing in the Gaelic my grandmother had taught me, I crawled on, and the sound of the helicopter faded into the distance.

Later I discovered they'd had three choppers and a company of infantry out looking for me, along with Reese, Chalky and Eddie. My navigation was all fucked up. I hadn't been consulting my wrist compass often enough and when I had I wasn't clear-headed enough to follow the direction I needed to for more than a few yards, concentrating instead on putting my head down and keeping moving. So I had actually zigzagged my way north, covering three yards for every one in the right direction, and I was still half a mile from the RV and had my nose pointed to the east of it. I'm damned glad I didn't know that at the time, though – it would have been the last straw.

As it was, I came out of the rain forest and hit another patch of *belukar*. I lay there in the sunlight for a while. The last morphine shot had worn off and now I was clenching my teeth against the pain and trying to gasp for breath at the same time. The maggots were welling out from under both my field dressings, fat and white, and I was covered in leeches. My own mother wouldn't have recognized me, and I was very near to just lying back and giving up. Then I heard the helicopter again.

I knew this was my last chance and my hands were slipping and shaking as I got the smoke grenade off my belt. I broke a nail trying to straighten the pin on the damn thing, but then, as the chopper's engines rose to a roar, I finally yanked out the pin and tossed the grenade as far as I could, which wasn't far. In seconds I was surrounded by choking purple smoke. Cursing my stupidity, I crawled upwind of it.

The chopper was there. I remember looking up at the thundering shadow silhouetted by the sun and grinning like a madman. They couldn't land, so they were lowering a harness to me. It caught on a bush, lifted up again, and finally was a foot off the ground, less than two yards away. I struggled towards it, swearing, and got it under my armpits, then gave the thumbs up. I began to lift off the ground.

That's it, I thought. I've made it.

But there was one more little indignity to undergo.

As I rose above the trees I was holding the SLR by the barrel, like an idiot. My hands were slippery and weak as water. I remember the damn thing sliding through my grasp with me glaring after it, and then – zip! – it was gone down into the *ulu*, irrecoverable. I was so pissed off that when they finally got me into the chopper I wanted to go down after it again, so they tell me. I was sure I had made a complete arse of myself, and didn't know how I would meet my mates' eyes when I got back to safety. Then, thank God, I passed out.

Shoot and Scoot was quietly binned after that, a decision that came from the bottom up. But it would resurface as an SOP ten years later. In Borneo.

2

April 1963

The whys and wherefores of conflict have never been a major concern of mine, even though they may have got me shot from time to time. As I saw my job back in '63, it had nothing to do with politics. But politics was what it had been all about in Malaya, and it would prove to be the same in Borneo.

A Squadron had gone out there at the start of the year, and we in D were sure we were next, so Hereford was as busy as a hive, with everyone trying to nick little pieces of kit they were sure would save their lives, or at least make them more comfortable, in the jungle. There is no creature on earth as acquisitive as the British soldier. If it isn't nailed down, he'll have it. He believes in pinching for a rainy day, so to speak, whereas his quartermaster's job is to see that he gets as little equipment as possible, and that in all the wrong sizes.

Fortunately, the latter wasn't true for the SAS. As soon as we were sure we were next in line for a Borneo tour, the QM's stores opened up like Aladdin's cave and out flowed a cornucopia of goodies. And, of course, there were those keen souls who paid out of their own pocket for the truly awesome articles which the British Army would never stock in a thousand years, they being superbly made and very expensive. Things like American jungle boots, which many thought better than our DMS boots; personal insect repellent – the type that, unlike the standard-issue stuff, actually keeps insects away; and mossie nets, hammocks, silk socks, wicked-looking knives. Me, I just made do with the issue kit. It's my experience that after a few months in the field the difference the fancy stuff makes to your life is undetectable.

In the years since Malaya I had remained with the Regiment by the skin of my teeth. I was thirty months recovering from that day's events, but eventually I made it back to full fitness, and insisted on doing Selection again to prove it. (I must have been knocked on the head somewhere in the jungle.) By 1963 I was a sergeant with D Squadron, one of the old hands who had fought through Malaya. B Squadron had been disbanded after the Emergency, so it was just ourselves and A. We had 16, 17, 18 and 19 Troops, whereas A had 1, 2, 3 and 4. Don't ask about the numbers. It's ancient history. D Squadron was at a strength of about seventy officers and men, but we were never able to fill every position we needed – there were just never enough men getting badged. Each troop consisted of sixteen men, usually broken down into four four-man teams in which one was a signaller, one a medic, one usually a linguist and one a demolitionist or other specialist. We were a tight bunch. Chalky White was still in my troop, still full of crap jokes, still the pill-pusher of the party. But Eddie Baker and Reese had left. There were younger men coming in now – as young as I had been in Malaya, I suppose – and they were still largely untried. For some of them, Borneo would provide their first whiff of gunsmoke.

But why Borneo?

It was John Woodhouse's fault that we were sent there, of course. As soon as the 'Confrontation' had begun (why must they always think up these stupid names for small wars?), our esteemed lieutenant colonel had rung up General Walker out in the east and put us at his disposal. He had more or less rebuilt the postwar SAS, had our John, and now he was keen as mustard to see it in action again. He was a good man, a tough bastard who got stuck in along with his lads at every opportunity – sometimes when he shouldn't have been there at all.

The Confrontation was the fault of the new President of Indonesia, Sukarno. He didn't like the Brits at all, what with our empire and military bases close by. He envisaged a great Asian Community, a bit like the EEC only with more guns and himself as supreme head. And the British presence in Malaysia didn't tie in with his plans one bit. Communism again, of course. Sukarno flirted with it, and the Chinese were rabble-rousing in the area too, with cells of the so-called Clandestine Communist Organization (CCO) in all the cities, but primarily in Sarawak.

The border between the British territories of Sabah, Brunei and Sarawak and the rest of Indonesia, or Kalimantan as the south of the Borneo landmass was called, was nine hundred miles long. To defend it, Walker had six infantry battalions, plus some local odds and sods. If he'd lined them all up the length of the border there would have been one man every four hundred yards. Not good. So our job – all seventy of us – was to 'dominate the jungle'. In other words, to do a pretty similar job to the one we'd done in Malaya, getting to know the natives, and managing to be in the right place at the right time without a lot of aimless patrolling in between.

Easy said. The fact was that there were parts of the border so wild they had never been explored, much less surveyed and mapped. In all the maps of the area we were given, there were big blank spaces that no white man had ever penetrated. We didn't even know if they were inhabited. It was all real *Boy's Own* stuff, and the lads lapped it up.

General Walker couldn't police a border like that, so the idea was that he'd keep the regular infantry back in the rear areas, ready to respond to any enemy incursions at a moment's notice. But to do that he had to have some kind of early-warning system out along the border to let him know when the bad guys were in the neighbourhood. And that was where the SAS came in. We were to be the eyes and ears of the British Army in Borneo, gathering every scrap of information that was going, by getting on the right side of the locals and persuading them that the Indos were bad news. Not only that, but we were to fill in those blank spaces in the maps, and chart out the whole length of the border. A combination of social workers, mapmakers and explorers, we really had our work cut out for us. But looking at the featureless spaces on the maps in Hereford, even I felt a little tingle of excitement, despite the fact that I was going back into the jungle.

I had got married in the time between Malaya and Borneo, but it hadn't really worked out. It's a rare woman who can share her husband with the Regiment, and put up with the long absences, the lack of explanation and the knowledge that her other half is probably closer to the blokes in his troop than he is to her. We hadn't divorced – this was still only 1963, remember – but I hadn't seen her in about six months and didn't even have a phone number. It felt kind of odd to be buggering off to the other side of the world – and perhaps not coming back – with no one to wave you off. But the excitement and frustration and hectic, last-minute preparations drove her out of my mind. That's the thing about the Regiment – there's always something to do, and if there isn't, then you're not doing your job properly. And the lads are always there for each other, only to joke about it in the bar afterwards. That's the strength of an SAS squadron, but it's also what made some of the things that were to happen to us so hard to take.

3

I had forgotten the heat.

The sheer suffocating nature of tropical heat
has to be experienced to be believed. Back in the
UK it was a chilly springtime, after one of the
harshest winters on record. We disembarked at
Kuching in Sarawak and immediately were in a
muck sweat, and we were to remain in a muck
sweat for the rest of our tour.

Things were hotting up. A Squadron before
us had had a largely uneventful tour, and
had concentrated mainly on doing good deeds
for the Iban natives and inserting themselves
seamlessly into the life of the jungle. But just
as we arrived the CCO got cocky and raided
a police station at Tebedu in Sarawak, killing
one copper, wounding two others and making
off with the contents of the armoury. Tebedu
was only two miles from the border, so there
had been no chance of an early warning, and it
was the Queen's Royal Irish Hussars who were

first on the scene – in armoured cars, no less. But they were too late to catch any of the cheeky buggers who had been there. The enemy had hit and run, disappearing across the frontier.

So the Confrontation was being stepped up, which was fine with us. From now on, British patrolling was to be more aggressive, and we were even to instigate Reactive Observation Posts when we felt they were appropriate – another term for an ambush in the SAS book.

The Sultan of Brunei, Sandhurst-educated, was dead keen to help the British operation, and he loaned the Regiment a house to operate from. The place was a big, austere, rambling affair which the Japanese had used as their headquarters in the Second World War. They had tortured a young girl to death there, and her spirit was supposed to haunt the place. The locals shunned its vicinity, which was all to the good, and the Haunted House, as it came to be known, was to be the Regiment's base in Brunei for the next two and a half years.

Each troop was given an area of responsibility, and ours turned out to be a place in south-western Sabah on the Pensiangan front. Long Pa Sia was its name, and south of the town itself the border with Kalimantan bulged out in a salient which was furrowed with rivers, densely jungled and lined with ridges that went up to three thousand feet – the height of Snowdon. The rivers flowed south, into Indonesia, and one, the Salilir, paralleled the border for close on twenty miles, providing excellent communications for the four Indonesian military posts along it – Lipaha, Nantakor, Lumbis and Sakikilo. The local tribe, the Muruts, were not a hundred per cent friendly to us because there were so many Indonesian soldiers close by and they didn't want to be punished for fraternizing with the 'enemy'. So it would be an uphill struggle, literally and figuratively, but the Long Pa Sia Bulge had to be taken under British control.

Myself, Chalky White, a youngster named Paddy Brooke who was from Northern Ireland and was our signaller, and Pete Conlan, our demo expert, were inserted into the Bulge in the third week of August 1963.

I couldn't help thinking of Malaya. The heat, the noises and above all the smell brought the events of some ten years ago flooding back, which was downright annoying. But at the same time, I was remembering all I had learned before, all the jungle lore that it had taken months to accumulate. And it was my job now to impart it to the two inexperienced members of the team, Paddy and Pete.

So we had a jock, a mick and two Sassenachs on

the team – a nice mix. We had worked and trained together before shipping out, and had taken the measure of each other's personalities at an early stage, both in the field and propping up the bar. I knew that Paddy was a quiet, intense young man who was obsessed with getting everything right. He looked after the Clansman radio as though it was his favourite niece, and he was good at coaxing signals from the ether in the most unlikely places, farting about with it until he homed in on Zero's faint voice. That would be important, as there were swathes of ground in Borneo where radios simply ceased to function, all signals blocked by the steep ridges that ran up and down the country. In addition, dampness got into the sets very quickly, rendering them useless – a problem that would not be solved until some boffin or other brought out a new waterproofed radio, which, with the glacial rate of innovation in the MOD, would probably be around the turn of the next century.

Pete Conlan was a Brummie who loved blowing things up, pure and simple. He was never happier than when he was messing about with C4 explosive and bits of wire and detonators, and he had confided to me that, given half a chance, he'd like to try his hand at setting up a few booby-traps for the opposition. That was out of the question at the moment, but I had mentioned it to the OC, Major Curtiss, and he had seemed rather ghoulishly interested in the notion. That's the way to do things in the Regiment – you plant a little seed of an idea in the officers' heads and let it quietly germinate.

Chalky White I knew as well as – better than – I had my own wife. Despite his fondness for profoundly unfunny jokes, I knew him to be a sound man. If he ever left the Regiment he wanted to be some kind of paramedic – he had a library of medical books four feet long back in Hereford – but he was also uncannily calm when the bullets began to fly. In fact combat seemed to make Chalky withdrawn and thoughtful, whereas it turns most men into headless chickens, or at least quickens their blood, as it does mine.

We were all in the Regiment for different reasons, but the thing we had in common was that we were all desperately keen. There was cynicism in the ranks back then, of course, and a lot of finger-pointing, but if you had taken the average trooper and put the thumbscrews on him he would have at last admitted that our outfit was the best in the world, and there was no point being anywhere else. There was also a common love of sheer excitement and variety among us that is impossible to explain. It was and is crazy to want to do the things we did, but we were never happy doing anything else. Like I said, impossible to explain, and if you tried to probe a group of troopers about it you'd get laughed out of the bar.

The roar of the little Whirlwind's rotors died away, and the four of us were alone with the jungle. We'd legged it out of the clearing that was the DOP and were now lying in All-Round Defence in a patch of *belukar* with the mossies just becoming gleefully aware of our presence and zooming in like Lancasters on a German dam.

Back in the *ulu* again, with that tremendous feeling of awareness that only comes with being on active service. Not fear, but a somehow more vivid sense of being alive.

I was still using the good old SLR, because I liked its power and reliability, as did Chalky. But Paddy and Pete had both opted for 5.56mm M16s, the black plastic rifle of the US Army that was starting to see service in Vietnam. You get a higher rate of fire from the M16, but the damn thing is so bloody fragile, and it jams easily if it's dirty, whereas you could hammer an SLR over an anvil all day and then shoot with it all night. Since Pete was going to be point man most of the time, it made sense that he had an automatic weapon, for if we were bumped it was a case of Shoot and Scoot – he'd lay down as much fire as possible and then run like hell.

A lot of the lads weren't happy with this SOP. As in Malaya, they didn't like the thought of leaving any of their mates – or their mates' bodies – behind. Eventually the SOPs would change, as a result of several fire-fights and the attitudes of the troopers themselves.

But all that was in the future. For the moment, we were to avoid contact and simply get the feel of the ground and the locals. I had a journal with me which I was supposed to fill with information on the area and its inhabitants, for all the world like some glorified travel writer.

We were travelling light, carrying perhaps sixty pounds of kit apiece. Later that would be seen to be too much weight for a man to carry all day in the jungle, and the maximum would become fifty. This was a real bitch for big blokes like me, who can honestly carry more, and who besides need the extra rations to keep them going.

We had ruminated for hours over what we should take and what we should leave behind. In the end each of us took the standard personal items – an escape compass, paper money sewn into our clothing in slim plastic bags in case we needed the help of the locals in an emergency, field dressings, morphine (supposedly two ampoules per man, but I made sure we had six apiece – Malaya had taught me that much), torch, notebook, pencil, map (unmarked, of course), knife, watch, matches (in plastic), bog-roll, and for me, a well-waterproofed paperback novel.

That was on our person. On our belts we each had two full mags, two water bottles, puritabs, two rat-packs, hexamine stove, wire-saw, paludrine, insect repellent, spoon, mess tin, rifle-cleaning kit and one grenade, though I was lugging two extra smoke grenades, just in case.

And then there were our bergens. Paddy, the poor bugger, was lumbered with the radio, twelve pounds of metal and wires which was to be preserved from harm at all costs. Then there were spare batteries, of course – and we're not talking little Ever-Readys here. The spare battery for a Clansman is the size and weight of three bricks, and a real drag at the bottom of your bergen.

Each of us also had a SARBE. All we had to do was set the rescue beacon off and the Whirlibird cavalry would arrive to hoist us out of the shit. That was the theory anyway.

We also all carried parachute-silk sleeping bags, spare socks, shirt and so on, as well as extra rat-packs and hexamine tablets for the little cookers. Chalky, of course, had the medic's kit – surgical instruments, plasters and bandages, and all sorts of drugs to combat the various nasties floating around the environment.

And we had two water bags which we filled just before we holed up for the night, because to camp near a river at night in the jungle is asking for trouble. Rivers are the highways of the jungle for both animals and men. We filled the bags at night because they would be needed first thing in the morning for cooking, washing and filling up water bottles. We never watered at the same place twice, and we always bivvied down at least a mile from where we had drawn water. Similarly, any rubbish in the form of left-over tins or papers from our morning's ablutions would be carried away from the bivvy site and buried at least an hour's march later – buried bloody deep too, otherwise the wild pigs would dig it up.

Our daily rations weighed one pound per man, giving us 2000 calories. Not a lot. We needed more like 4000 a day to retain our body weight, so it was an accepted fact that a patrol in the jungle for extended periods that did not partake of the hospitality of friendly locals would come back looking like a bunch of anorexics. Often, a team which was about to go on a two- or three-week patrol would stuff themselves silly back at the Haunted House so as to create something like a camel's hump to live off in the jungle. The US Army sees it differently – they think a man should enter the jungle as lean as possible. And we all know how successfully they wage war in jungles.

D Squadron had been both lucky and unlucky in the timing of their tour. A, who had been in before us, had had a whale of a time. There had been little enemy activity then, and the lads from A had just inserted themselves into the jungle and lived with the locals for three or four months, happy as pigs in shit, getting drunk on *tapai*, a kind of foul rice wine, and stuffing themselves with *jarit*. Which, come to think of it, was something of an ordeal after all, because *jarit* is possibly one of the most disgusting concoctions ever dreamt up as food. Try and imagine raw pork, salt and rice buried in a length of bamboo for a month and then unearthed and eaten. The only way the A Squadron boys could get it down was to get stinking drunk on *tapai* first. My heart bled for them, it really did.

In any case, they'd had a kind of Robinson Crusoe experience among the innocent natives, doctoring the babies and getting to know the headmen and building up a very useful body of information about the country in general. But things were different. Ever since Tebedu the shit had begun splattering the fan, and we were in a real conflict type of situation. So, no more sitting about getting drunk with the Muruts – or at least not very much – as there was a job of work to be done.

Since this was our first patrol, we were more or less just getting our bearings. We'd inserted just north of the River Plandok, right in the heart of the Long Pa Sia Bulge, and we were to parallel the river's course south for about six miles until we came to the border, then mooch about down there for a while and beetle off back home again. Simple.

It looked simple on the map, at any rate. But we found as we went along that maps were not wholly to be trusted, and that just half a mile on paper can be a complete fucking nightmare in reality.

The land was up and down, up and down, and we couldn't contour round any ridges because it could have stuffed our navigation, so it was nose to the ground and get up the hills, then back down again, and so on ad infinitum and ad nauseam. We were pretty much all right for the first part of the patrol because we just had to keep the river on our right, and even with all the jungle clamour it was possible to hear it foaming away between its banks as it raced towards the border, cutting fantastic gullies and canyons in the ridges, which in turn were matted with dense jungle. So it was impossible to go in a straight line for more than five feet at a time, and we sometimes had to hack a way for ourselves with our parangs, leaving a trail a blind man could have followed. Still, the good news was, we didn't encounter any other trails heading in the same direction, though we crossed more than one pig trail which led down to the river and kept us on our toes.

Navigation. In Borneo its importance could not be overemphasized. With crap maps, rugged country and an enemy who at the start at least knew the country much better than we did, it had to be absolutely spot on.

We would march for fifty minutes in every hour and then halt for the other ten to get our bearings and just tune in to the jungle. Pete was navigating up front, with me check-navigating. As a rule, when you're tabbing through the really thick stuff, hacking a passage as often as not, and still trying not to make too much of a disturbance, then you'll travel perhaps 1000 yards in an hour. That's less than two-thirds of a mile for every back-breaking, sweat-soaking, leech-sucking hour of agonizing labour. When you're on a track, you don't just saunter down it like you're at Butlins, and so you make better time – 2000 yards an hour. But it's still a pace my old granny could beat if she were hobbling along the strand back home.

Pacings and bearings, the old mantra of Army navigation. Even if you didn't recognize a single terrain feature around you from the map, as long as you knew which direction you had taken and how far it had been, you were usually all right. So both Pete and I counted our paces, and we took a quick bearing every minute or so, sighting on a rock or a large tree or something. On Salisbury Plain you could take a bearing on a feature a mile away, but here it was more likely to be five yards.

Six hours' marching a day was the maximum – anything more and you'd just knacker yourself. So we covered perhaps four miles that first day, which sounds pitiful, but it illustrates the difficulties of fighting a little war in such country.

We backtracked along our trail and laid a snap ambush that evening, just in case. I was uneasy at the thought of all the hacking and grunting we'd been doing. It seemed almost sacrilegious. Then we lay for half an hour just listening to the rain forest, straining to hear or see anything even remotely out of the ordinary. But there was nothing. So I picked a bivvy site on the slopes of the ridge that lay east of the river, and we prepared to set up our bashas – one per two men. We took it in turns to open out the little hexamine stoves and brew up. Tea, army biscuits and tinned meat. What you do with the last is take off both ends of the tin and then push out the cylinder of meat inside, cutting off burger-like slices as it emerges. Spam smells almost like bacon when it's fried in the mess tin that way.

It's not exactly a sylvan idyll, sleeping out in the jungle – not as the SAS do it at any rate. Before night routine began, Paddy had to send the second of our two signals of the day back to Zero. Three missed signals, for whatever reason, and they'd come out looking for us, which was a comforting thought, but also meant you couldn't afford to be cavalier about calling in.

He used Morse code, as it utilized the longer-range High Frequencies rather than the shorter but more complicated communications you get with Ultra High. Of course, if we got in a scrape, it was bugger Morse code, and we'd be yelling into the handset, but since we were at leisure, relatively speaking, it was just fine. And besides, Paddy took an arcane delight in Morse, the radiospeak of former wars.

After comms were taken care of and everyone had fed, we washed, stowed the radio for moving and set up the two bashas. At all times there would be no light and only the bare minimum of sound, and weapons had to remain at hand always. I basha'd up with Paddy, as I was the team leader and he was the signaller, and Chalky bedded down with Pete. I set 'stags' of course, every man doing at least an hour of sentry duty before daylight, with myself the last man on before stand-to, just before dawn.

Night would swoop down in the space of five minutes. Pitch-darkness, and just the jungle noises all around and the looming impression of the great trees all about our heads, with the river foaming off in the night. In Malaya we'd sometimes been allowed a candle on a stick at night to read by, but that was out of the question here. We had eleven hours of darkness on average, which at least meant everyone had a chance to get a lot of sleep, but the problem was that it is hard to sleep in the jungle. It's something to do with being in such a *busy* place. Every five fucking minutes there's something howling or crashing through the trees or wailing like it's lost its mum. Then there's the clammy touch of a tiger leech on your neck. Three inches long, bright orange on the undersides with green stripes on top, they look like something from another world, and in a sense they are.

'Bloody madhouse,' Paddy murmured beside me.

I looked at him. His eyes were open – I could see them shining faintly in the dark. 'What do you think of the *ulu* then?' I whispered.

I could see him shake his head slightly. 'Heck of a place for a bloody war, so it is. Can they not fight somewhere civilized, with a bar nearby?'

'Oh, don't,' I groaned. 'Imagine a cold beer now, with the condensation trickling down the outside of the glass . . .'

The heat was as heavy as a shroud and we could feel things crawling all over us in the darkness. The entire complement of Noah's Ark seemed to be out there in the night screeching their lungs off.

'How's the radio?' I asked Paddy. I was wide awake now.

'Damp's getting into it already. Whole bloody thing ought to be put in a plastic bag when they issue it.'

'We'll just have to cook it then,' I said.

'What?'

'Cook it over a hexi stove to get the damp out.'

'You're joking!'

'No – we did it in Malaya. It's the only way to keep the bastards functioning on a long patrol.'

Paddy chuckled softly.

A low voice came from just outside our basha – Chalky's low growl. He was on stag.

'Are you two lovebirds on your honeymoon or what? Jock, just give him one up the arse and stop chatting him up.'

'You're just fucking jealous,' I told Chalky,

'because I gave you something you'd never known before, you butch little bitch.'

I could hear Chalky trying to smother his laughter. We all should have been silent as graves at night, of course, but Christ, we were only human.

First light found us packed up and leaning on our bergens, rifles in the shoulder. Throughout history, men have attacked other men at dusk and dawn. God knows why. But the British Army in the field quite sensibly goes on alert for an hour before dusk and an hour before dawn, just in case. I've always thought that all it would take some day is some bugger familiar with our SOPs, and he could come crashing in on any British outfit in the world just after stand-to and catch the whole shebang on their arses sipping a morning brew.

Tea, biscuits and a tin of bloody sardines – that was breakfast. We didn't shave or wash, as we didn't want any soapy smells wafting around us as we made our way through the jungle, so it was an increasingly malodorous crew that set off that morning with the rising sun in our left eye and the sound of the river still off to the right.

We were travelling through alternating patches of primary jungle and *belukar*, so the parangs were in periodic use, but in general we tried to keep it as sneaky-beaky as possible and as a result our pace was awesomely slow. We made perhaps a mile and a half in the first three hours. But this was a hot area, the southern part of the Bulge, and every step took us closer to the border.

It rained in the early afternoon, a battering, torrential downpour that brought a mountain of muck and a legion of creepy-crawlies out of the canopy overhead, so that there were things wiggling down the backs of our shirts for the rest of the day. Then Chalky actually uttered what I gleefully interpreted as a yelp of fright as a sodding great python went slithering along a branch directly over his head when we halted to check our bearings. He insisted it was an involuntary intake of breath, and I told him to check for chocolate in his trousers.

Soaked to the bone but still sweating like bastards, we moved on. The land was like a concertina, up and down all over the place, but in general we were gaining altitude. There was a ridge running roughly parallel with the border which spawned rivers running out north and south, and we were approaching its northern slopes. Once we were at the top of the ridge Indonesia would be a stone's throw away, and the patrol would have reached the farthest limit of its march. We would follow the ridge west and east for a few days and then begin the tab back north to the pick-up point.

I had my eye on Pete's back as we laboured carefully onward, when he raised his hand and then batted it towards the ground.

We went to ground immediately. Pete was on his belly now, staring intently over the barrel of his M16 at something ahead. Finally he turned round, put three fingers on his arm and raised that hand to his head. Translation: 'Sergeant, on me now.'

I dumped my bergen and crawled forward. When I was beside him he simply pointed.

Something was out there in the jungle – something big, like a longhouse, but overgrown-looking. A line of them, in fact. It was impossible to make out anything beyond general shapes in the chaotic riot of vegetation around us. Definitely man-made, though, as the shapes were rectangular.

I waved up to the rest of the team and we went into All-Round Defence, everybody's ankles crossed over the man's next to him so that a signal could be passed with a series of foot taps and never a word said.

We lay there for perhaps a quarter of an hour, the sweat dripping off our noses and our bellies pressed into the muddy jungle floor, leeches crawling up our wrists. I was in bloody

Malaya again, waiting to step into that clearing, about to get blown away. My hip ached with the memory.

Pete looked at me at last, and I nodded reluctantly. We moved up into a line to cover him as he rose noiselessly to his feet and then inched forward at a crouch, rifle in the shoulder and muzzle following his line of sight.

Nothing happened.

He moved on, and even at that moment I had to admire his woodcraft. He was quiet as a snake. He went to ground just yards from the strange, jungle-wrapped shapes, studying them intently. Finally he stood up straight, gave the thumbs up and motioned us forward.

We joined him in silence. The shapes were really big up close, and I could see the glimmer of broken glass under the creepers.

'What the hell?'

'It's a train, Jock. A bloody steam train and a set of carriages, out here in the middle of nowhere.'

I yanked away a section of creeper and, sure enough, there was a rusted wheel beneath and a section of rail. I pulled myself up with a rotting handrail and found myself in the engine. The boiler door was open, and there were still gauges and levers to be seen, all half hidden by mould.

'Four carriages,' Pete told me from below. 'Not derailed or anything, but the rails it's on just peter out. Someone just seems to have forgotten about the thing. Unreal.'

Then Chalky's face was thrust through the matted vegetation that surrounded the engine. 'Jock – you'd best come and have a look at this,' he said. His face was grim.

I left the train and followed him perhaps fifteen yards into the jungle. Things were sticking out of the ground there, with bamboo sprouting beside them and huge ferns shrouding them.

I bent down to have a closer look, and found a rotting wooden board on a stick thrust into the ground.

'What the . . . ?' Letters carved into the board. A European name, hardly legible, and below it, 'Australian and New Zealand Army Corps'.

'Shit,' I whispered.

'There's hundreds of them, Jock,' Chalky told me. 'It's a bloody cemetery – one no bugger has ever found. Must have been the Japs in the last war – but no one in Kuching or Brunei has ever heard of anything like this in this area.'

'They'll hear of it now,' I said, rising. 'Mark it on your map, Chalky. Take a good set of bearings.'

'But . . .'

'I know, but we won't be letting out any

national secrets if they find this place. Stick it on the bloody map. These men are owed that much.'

Chalky shook his head. 'Poor bastards. Wonder if anyone ever missed them.'

It was a sombre place, and I didn't like to think of what had brought these men here, and what had killed them. I liked even less to think of them lying here all this time untended, unknown, the wild pigs rooting up their graves. Even the jungle seemed quieter in this spot. I've noticed that before – the wild things know when something unpleasant has happened in a spot, and avoid it. Take the place where the Nazi concentration camp used to be at Belsen – it's just a beautiful European woodland now, and all that's left of what happened there is a load of mounds in the middle of it, but no birds ever sing in the trees there, and wildlife shuns the place.

'Time to move on,' I said brusquely. I didn't want the lads – or myself for that matter – dwelling on this too much. We had a hike ahead of us before dark.

4

For some reason we were more on edge after our little encounter with the lost train and its guardians. The land we were travelling through became rocky in places, and the jungle was more open, so we made better time. Thanks to our altitude, comms were fine, and we sent our daily messages with no trouble. But we were still wary, as though waiting for something to jump out from behind a tree at us. It happens, in the jungle. A man can become so attuned to the environment that he knows something is wrong even before he's realized what the reason for the knowledge is. But we'd only been out a couple of days.

We basha'd up the second night without incident, all too knackered to do anything but grab some gonk and then stagger up for our stint on sentry when we were due. Just before dawn, as I took my stag, there was a thunderstorm across the border in Indonesia. I could hear it. When the sun came up it was immediately hidden in rolling, slate-grey cloud, and the air was almost too heavy to breathe. I had the feeling we were in for a day of it, and hustled the team as much as I could through breakfast and packing up, so that we were on our way again while it was barely light.

All morning we toiled up the ridge, while the sky grew darker and darker over our heads. For once, Paddy couldn't get Zero on the radio, which I put down to all the meteorological activity that was swirling around us, but it made me uneasy all the same. We'd had perfect comms up to now – a rarity on most patrols – and we were approaching the border. I didn't like losing touch with base.

Around midday we got to the summit of the ridge, just as the storm broke. The sky erupted in jagged chains of forked lightning, while the thunder crashed as loud as an artillery barrage. And then it began to rain. Huge drops of water came down thicker and thicker until they were roaring down on us and it was difficult to breathe and virtually impossible to see. We holed up in a pocket of large trees and boulders on the north side of the ridge while streams of water ran down around our ankles – the run-off from the ridge-top – and were scarcely able to hear one another shout in the racket. There was no point in struggling on for the meantime – it would be too easy to wander over to the wrong side of the border. So we sat and endured it and watched the storm lash the jungle like the wrath of God. It was quite enjoyable really. We had to stay hidden, but there was no danger of giving away our position through noise. Which was just as well, as we all laughed our bollocks off when Paddy leapt a yard in the air, gibbering. A bloody great scarlet and amber snake had slithered between his legs as he crouched in the rain, washed away and trying to save itself by coiling round his ankle.

It was Pete who saw him, nothing more than a shadow in the rain at first. He nudged me and nodded up the side of the ridge, giving me a thumbs down, meaning 'enemy'.

Immediately we were all rifles in the shoulder, humour gone. Pete must have had a bloody hawk for a mother – I couldn't see a damn thing in the roar and pummel of the torrential rain. But then movement caught my eye and there he was. A Murut tribesman picking his way down the ridge with a little mouse deer slung over his shoulder and a bamboo blowpipe in his free hand. Out bagging his dinner by the looks of things, and what was more, he was coming from the direction of the border. If he knew that area well enough to hunt there, then it was worthwhile trying to talk to him.

So I stood up. He was about fifty yards away, and half invisible in the rain. If the jungle had been thick we'd never even have known he'd passed us.

He froze like a rabbit caught in headlights, zooming in on the movement as I had done. I held up an open hand, for all the world like I was John Wayne meeting some Indians, and shouted above the downpour, '*Selamat Petang, ada baik lah?*' Which translates as 'Good afternoon, how's it going?' or something like that.

He remained staring at me, obviously ready to bolt, and I hastily shouted out that we were British soldiers, not Indonesians. He was visibly relieved, and padded forward. The British were all right, he said. They had helped some children in a village in the valley below – that would have been A Squadron doing their hearts and minds stuff – and they'd had had sweets for the kids too. But the Indonesians were a right bunch of awkward bastards, and didn't like him hunting anywhere south of the Long Pa Sia ridge, where his family had hunted for all time, because they had bases there.

We sat down opposite each other, chummy as anything, while the rest of the team quietly moved out to cover the approach down the ridge. His name was Krusin, he told me, and had I any sweets he could take back to his village for the children?

The rain was at last easing off at this point, so we didn't have to shout. Unfortunately, all I had to give good old Krusin was a tin of sardines, which he had obviously seen before and was not too impressed with. I asked him about the land to the south of the ridge along the border and he said that there were always soldiers moving north from the two Indo bases at Pa Fani and Long Tapadong, down two tracks which led right to the border. The two bases were also beside two rivers, and there was much river traffic to keep them supplied. Apparently it was all busy as a beehive in that part of the jungle, and he was cheesed off because it was frightening away all the game. Not like nice British soldiers, who moved very quietly – quiet as a Murut.

All this was fascinating stuff, and I privately made up my mind to bring Krusin a bloody great bar of chocolate on our next patrol, though it'd be brown sludge by the time we got it to him. I asked him where his village was, and he said not far, would we like to go there?

Do bears shit in the woods? I told him we'd be honoured, and so he led off and we followed.

'Not far' is relative when you're carrying a rifle and a bergen and webbing and you've already had a day of it. It seemed pretty bloody far to me at least when we finally reached a cluster of longhouses in a tiny clearing, about a mile and a half to the north-west. Something else for the Squadron Intelligence boys to stick on their maps.

It was more of a hamlet than a village, with perhaps six or seven longhouses and a cluster of smaller huts. Some naked and wide-eyed children watched us march in, agog, and a filthy toddler pissed himself and began to cry. Krusin was as proud as Pontius Pilate as the rest of the villagers – there couldn't have been more than thirty all told – gathered around us and he introduced us as his new mates, very nice British soldiers.

They were an unprepossessing bunch, naked but for loincloths, some of the children covered in sores and half-domesticated pigs rooting around their heels. The animals lived under the stilt-mounted longhouses, and fed partly on the shit that the villagers dropped down from above. I caught Pete staring at the nude torso of a nubile young woman and hissed out of the corner of my mouth, 'Stop staring at her tits, for fuck's sake, or they'll end up giving her to you.'

'You what?'

'They've been known to give away their daughters out of politeness, but we can't accept. It makes the young men jealous.'

'Fuck me pink. I'll bet it does.'

*   *   *

The patrol had not been meant to be a hearts and minds op, just an intelligence-gathering mission, but I reasoned to myself that we could probably learn more from Krusin and his fellow villagers about the area in an afternoon than we could in days of hiking about the place ourselves. Plus, since they were *there*, in our operational area, we had no choice but to befriend them. So the bergens came off and we squatted down in a stinking longhouse with the woodsmoke making our eyes smart and the village lovelies darting in to have a peek at us in a giggling procession, while Krusin – who turned out to be the headman – filled us in and plied us with bowls of *tapai*, which we were careful to drink slowly. We couldn't offend him by refusing, but there was no question of getting legless this close to the border with the Indos as active as Krusin made them out to be.

They're good people, the Muruts, simple and relatively honest. They didn't have the same relationship with the British as the Dyaks have because they were caught in the middle between the Brits and the Indos, and they had little choice but to sway in the prevailing wind. But they obviously preferred us to the Indos, even more so after Chalky got out his medic kit and began doctoring a hundred and one different ailments – everything from hookworm to dysentery.

We spent the night in the village, and I quietly set stags despite the friendliness of our hosts. Paddy radioed in our location and gave a situation report. Major Curtiss had no problems with my decision, but we were to head back north the next day – news travels fast in the jungle and it was likely the Indos would soon get to know there were British soldiers in their backyard. At that time we were not yet ready to get involved in any contacts.

We drew a fascinated audience as we stripped and cleaned our weapons, even dismantling and reloading the magazines. Krusin proudly showed us an old over-and-under shotgun he had inherited from his father and that he sometimes hunted with. Not very often, though, as he only had three shells to his name, and they looked dangerously mouldy and damp to me, which was why he still relied mainly on his blowpipe.

It was pretty packed in the longhouse as we lay down to sleep, everyone cheek by jowl and our eyes streaming from the smoke, the air full of the reek of the pigs below. I don't think I had been asleep for more than a couple of hours when Paddy picked a way through the snoring masses on the floor and told me it was my stag, the last one before stand-to. When I got outside the air seemed almost fresh by comparison. I had a few quiet minutes before the village came to life in the pre-dawn gloom, the women stirring up the fires and the men rubbing their eyes and pissing through the gaps in the longhouse floors. I roused the team and we packed up amid a crowd of onlookers, then bade our new friends goodbye, promising to return soon and protect them from the Indos. It was something of a relief when we set off on our own once more, north towards the pick-up point. We'd established a presence in the Bulge on our first patrol, and discovered a priceless source of information. All in all, not a bad start.

5

It took us two more careful and uneventful days to make our way back to the pick-up point, but the chopper arrived bang on time and ferried us back to Brunei. There were beers waiting for us back at the Haunted House, and we sipped them as we were debriefed, then trooped gratefully off to the showers. Major Curtiss delayed me a moment as the rest filed out. The beer was going straight to my head and I was shattered, filthy, covered in bites and scratches and with ominous rumblings coming from my bowels – probably the after-effects of the dreaded *tapai*.

'What's up, boss?' I asked Curtiss. He was a good man, devilishly keen to get the Squadron into the thick of it, as Woodhouse had been. He also got himself out in the field as much as he could – perhaps too often.

He was dressed in a pair of shorts and American jungle boots. We were still in the debriefing room, and an ancient fan turned slowly overhead, hardly making any difference to the heavy atmosphere inside. Curtiss wiped the sweat off his nose and flicked it away, grimacing.

'Thought I'd let you know, Jock – this is Rumour Control's info, nothing official, but it's quite likely that there's going to be a major incursion in your TAOR quite soon. The Indos have been building up in the Pensiangan Gap or thereabouts and also there are rumours that they're in the vicinity of Long Jawai in Sarawak. It's the Gurkhas there, as you know – we're too thin on the ground, and I had to pull Stainforth's team out and send it east – but this news of your Murut friend confirms my suspicions. I want you to go back there in two days and keep a close eye on the border south of Long Pa Sia. A company of the Leicesters are moving into the area – they'll be your back-up. If you come across anything, call them in and hit it hard. Of course, it's likely to be nothing, just the usual scaremongering, but it's as well to be sure.'

'OK, boss,' I said.

Two days. Oh well, I'd get at least one good night's sleep.

'Briefing here at 0900 hours tomorrow morning. Now get cleaned up and have a kip. You did a good job.'

* * *

SNAFU, it's called in the Army – Situation Normal: All Fucked Up. And then there's the next level – FUBAR: Fucked Up Beyond All Recognition. The situation in Borneo went to FUBAR early the next morning, when 150 Indonesian soldiers attacked the outpost of Long Jawai in Sarawak. The post was defended by six Gurkhas, six local coppers, and twenty-one of the indigenous Border Scouts, picked from the Dyaks, that the British Army was training up at the time. Five of the defenders were killed and the rest had to bug out, trekking through the jungle for four nerve-racking days to pass on the news. The 1st/2nd Gurkha Rifles responded at once with heli-borne troops and hit the Indos hard as they were retreating from the area, but it was a bit of a pyrrhic victory. Our intelligence had been absolute wank and there were a lot of red faces in Brunei. It also meant that my team was choppered out a day early, and so it was an irritable and still bone-tired bunch of blokes that the Whirlwind dropped off in the Long Pa Sia Bulge again that afternoon. We were out in the *ulu* once more.

Our orders this time gave us a little more cause for satisfaction, however. We were to tab up to the border and set up a Reactive OP, which meant that if any of the enemy came along we could engage them at our own discretion. So, despite

our tiredness, we were keyed up as we began the
weary march south towards the border. I had
even remembered the chocolate for Krusin.

Backing us up some eight miles to the rear
would be a company of the Royal Leicestershire
Regiment, based at the village of Long Pa Sia
itself. It was comforting to know that if we really
landed ourselves in the poo we could call in over
a hundred men in minutes, terrain permitting,
and both Pete and Chalky were full of beans on
the move south, eager to get stuck in. Chalky
and I were more thoughtful, however. What I'd
really have liked to have done was set up the OP
overlooking one of the two rivers which supplied
the two Indo bases just over the border, but that
would have meant crossing the border ourselves,
which was out of the question at that time. So
we'd have to settle for setting ourselves up on
the reverse slope of the ridge we'd climbed on
our last patrol, and await developments there.

It took us two days to get into position and
a third to recce the site for the OP and set
it up. Three days in total of back-breaking
work which had to be carried out in complete
silence. The strain was unbelievable. Have you
ever tried to use a machete quietly? We were
hacking down saplings which we would use to
build up a kind of hide when Paddy looked up
and raised a hand.

'Thought I heard something,' he hissed.

We all heard something then – a gasp of stifled agony from Pete. He'd been chopping at a stick he held in his left hand and such was his tension that Paddy's warning had made him miss the stick and hit his hand instead. There was a spurt of scarlet blood and Pete went ashen. I saw him clench his teeth together, the muscles bulging in his jaw. He didn't utter a sound except for a whispered and venomous 'Fuck!'

Chalky was on him in a moment, ripping open the first-aid kit, while Paddy and I crouched with our rifles in the shoulder, wide-eyed as deer. The jungle had gone quiet, even the shimmering backdrop noise of the insects stilled. I actually heard the pop as Chalky's needle began stitching its way through Pete's skin.

Fifteen minutes, and then the jungle sounds started up once more, and Chalky had put Pete's hand back together again. It was an ugly gash, but none of the tendons had been sliced, so it was more spectacular than dangerous. Chalky told me afterwards that he'd been in such a rush to get it sewn closed that he'd gone for the first needle in his bag, which happened to be a common sewing needle, not a medic's stitching one. That explained the popping sounds. Pete would heal, but he'd have a lumpy scar on the back of his hand to the end of his days.

Something had been out there in the jungle, though – we were all sure of it. We left the bergens in Pete's care and the three of us moved forward, stepping as carefully as though we were in a minefield. It was Paddy who found it, and he beckoned me over. There, in a patch of mud perhaps a hundred yards in front of the OP, was the track of a boot.

We cast about for more signs and found some snapped twigs, leaves crushed into the ground and finally some blurred footprints and a human turd along with some soiled pink toilet paper. Chalky and I looked at each other in disbelief, then bent to the ground and followed the tracks leading away from the spot.

They led south. We followed them for about four hundred yards. The passage of the bloke through the *belukar* was clear to see – Daniel Boone he was not – and we retraced his steps in single file, myself leading, then Chalkie and finally Paddy with the radio.

The *belukar* opened out and we found ourselves looking into a clearing of sorts, perhaps twenty yards wide. We sat down to scope it out, our hearts hammering. There was a camp in its midst, frames of branches making the skeletons of bashas, and, from where we lay, even cigarette ends were visible among the litter of the forest floor. I reckoned that it was a platoon-sized bivouac, and had been abandoned less than an hour before – the turdmaker must have been the last to bug out, in a hurry to catch up with his comrades.

I turned to Chalky, who smiled out of a filthy face and whispered, 'Christmas.'

We made our way back to the OP as quickly as we dared, me at the front raising my arms like a cross in the agreed signal so that Pete would not slot me on the way in. Then Chalky and I huddled up.

'We need the Leicesters,' I said.

'Obviously. But they'll never be able to chopper in on this terrain, and besides, the sound of the helis will give the game away.'

'So they hoof it,' I said thoughtfully.

'Yes. And they'll need a guide.'

We looked at each other. Was I to take the whole team back or just send two men and remain here with the fourth to keep an eye on things? We were so close here that I hated the idea of breaking off, but to leave two men alone in the presence of a platoon of the enemy was just not on. I sighed.

'We all go back, guide in the Leicesters and set up an ambush.'

'Jock, do you think they spotted us?'

I shook my head. 'The guy even took the time to wipe his arse, and they were smoking fags less than an hour before we came along. They're as innocent as the day is long.'

'Fuckers,' Chalky said with feeling. 'I hope they come back.'

'That's why they left the camp standing. Come on, let's get packed up.'

As the others started to get ready to move I called up Zero.

'Zero, this is Mike One Zero. Message over.'

Paddy's skill with the radio did not fail us. Major Curtiss's voice came back as loud as Whisper Mode permitted.

'Zero, send over.'

'Mike One Zero, 1645 hours, grid 345276, enemy camp located four-zero-zero south of my location, platoon strength. Am bugging out to call-sign Charlie Echo's location now with intention of guiding him back. Over.'

There was a pause as Curtiss digested this. Finally he came back: 'Roger your last, Mike One Zero. I will inform Charlie Echo of your intentions and set up an RV. Nice one. Over.'

'Mike One Zero, roger. Out.'

I looked over at Chalky and gave him the thumbs up, grinning.

Packing up was not just a case of stuffing our bits and pieces back in our bergens. The site of the abortive OP had to be returned to a virgin state, all parang scars smeared with mud, even the leaves replaced on the ground. By the time we had finished, the place looked as though mankind had never been near it, but the day was wearing on fast. Chalky took point, as Pete had been given a shot of morphine and was not a hundred per cent fit. We set out at as fast a pace as we could manage without blazing a trail or hacking down half the forest, but it was frustratingly slow all the same.

Curtiss came through on the radio again an hour later. He gave us a set of map co-ordinates to head to and wait for the Leicesters, who were already on the move. But there was no way they would reach us today – the choppers had dropped them off as far south into the jungle as they dared, but they were still miles short and would probably bivvy up in the jungle that night before rendezvousing with us the next day. It was the terrain's fault. We had helicopters, trucks and Land Rovers galore, the whole shooting match of a modern army's transport, but the jungle reduced everything to the speed of a walking man.

We bedded down for the night perhaps two miles from the RV location we had arranged with the Leicesters. There's no point blundering around in the *ulu* at night, especially with a bunch of trigger-happy squaddies out there too.

We had yellow bands on the insides of our hats and were supposed to turn them inside out for identification purposes, but a fat lot of good they'd be in the dark. We didn't set much store by them in daylight either.

I lay awake for a long time that night, smiling to myself as I recalled Pete's profane but *sotto voce* outrage when I had suggested he be medevacced. Tomorrow, with luck, we'd be in action.

6

After stand-to we packed up in a twinkling and were on our way again. I think we were almost as keyed up at the thought of running into the Leicesters as we were at the idea of the ambush we were hoping to pull off subsequently. To have a 'blue-on-blue', attacking each other by mistake, at this stage would be even more disastrous, with a substantial portion of the enemy setting up bases on the Sarawak side of the border at will. Cheeky bastards. The team were all a little outraged, I think, that these buggers had just come waltzing into our patch, smoking fags and shitting behind bushes as casual as you please. It was the fact that they were so unprofessional that annoyed us as much as anything else. They would pay for that lack of professionalism, in spades.

As soon as I gauged we were within a quarter of a mile of the RV we slowed down and I took over on point. When it came to it, the Leicesters weren't that hard to spot – you can't really hide thirty-odd men in the jungle. We could smell them, for a start. We could smell the soap off them from downwind. They were in All-Round Defence with platoon headquarters in the middle, and we sidled up to them like so many ghosts. I heard some prick cock his weapon at the sight of us and hiss, 'SAS – we're on your side, you twat!'

At least they didn't shout 'Who goes there?', but it was immediately clear to us that these blokes were as green as grass. They'd slashed a small clearing all the way around their position, laying waste the vegetation to create a field of fire. It seemed positively shocking to us, who'd been so careful to leave no trace of our presence ever since we'd been in the field.

I suppose our appearance had shocked them in their turn. They were fairly spruce, only having been out for a night, whereas we were dirty, unshaven and hollow-eyed. The only things about us that were clean were our weapons.

A young officer came up to me and I shook his outstretched hand. 'Lieutenant Peter Robinson,' he said. I could see him looking for badges of rank.

'Jock Ross, D Squadron,' I told him. 'You'd best get your men ready to move. We'll have to hustle if we're to get down to the ambush location before dark. I take it Zero has given you a sitrep?'

He nodded, a little nonplussed. 'Platoon strength, within half a mile of the border. But can we make it all the way down there in a day? It's rough country.'

'So I hear,' I said drily. 'But I want the ambush set up before dark. Today. There's no telling how long the enemy will stay north of the border – this could be an exploratory raid. I don't want to miss this one, Lieutenant.'

I think he had cottoned on to the fact that I was almost certainly a non-commissioned officer, but he couldn't have been any more than twenty, the Sandhurst shine still about him. He just nodded, and got his sergeant to start stirring up his men.

'Eight miles. A bit steep, even for us,' Chalky said. 'Think they'll hack it, Jock?'

'It's not a bloody Girl Guides get-together,' I retorted. 'We'll stuff moving quietly for most of it and concentrate on speed. This lot haven't got their jungle heads on yet anyway. Then the team will recce out the camp area before we let them within a mile of it, just to be sure.'

We set off at a cracking pace, having first made sure that the Leicesters cached their bergens. They were overloaded as it was, carrying too much food and not enough ammunition, but that could not be helped at this stage of the game. In the jungle the only two things you can never carry too much of are water and ammo. You can rub along on a tin of sardines and a few biscuits a day if you have to, but you're constantly losing pints of sweat. And if you're out for any length of time, resupply is so difficult that you should really carry all the ammo you possibly can, Shoot and Scoot notwithstanding.

So the Leicesters were suffering, plus they sounded like a herd of water-buffalo crashing through the jungle, and they stilled all the jungle noises for miles around. It wasn't their fault – they were fresh to the field, that was all. But it made the trek south a nerve-racking one for us troopers. The only comfort we had was that we had probably enough fire-power between us to deal with anyone who came to investigate.

We hammered along to their front, Chalky and I continually rechecking our line of march and pacings, the young Rupert, Robinson, doing the same – though they say the most dangerous thing on any battlefield is an officer with a map. Finally, when we decided we were within a mile of the enemy camp, we halted. Paddy and I went forward with our radio while the rest of the merry men had a breather. The Leicesters were soaked through, their faces scarlet, but they hadn't done badly at all. I was pretty well knackered myself.

It was a relief of sorts, though, to move silently again. Even though it was only the two of us, we felt somehow less vulnerable as we picked our way through the forest. I've always thought that the best way to really get to know any type of terrain is to fight in it. You can't be just a tourist, bimbling along; you have to become part of the country itself. And even if that sounds a little hippyish, it's a hundred per cent true, whether it's the jungle or the tundra.

So we moved up to the site of the enemy camp like a couple of panthers on the prowl – if panthers sweat like pigs and stink to high heaven.

It was still deserted, which was good, and by the looks of things they hadn't been back since their last visit. We crawled back from the rim of the clearing and I took the handset from Paddy.

'Charlie One Zero, this is Mike One Zero. Over.'

'Charlie One Zero, send. Over.'

'All clear, repeat, all clear. Move in. Over.'

'Roger. Out.'

It took them over an hour, and for the last twenty minutes we could hear them thrashing through the vegetation. I looked at Paddy and he rolled his eyes. Chalky brought the Rupert up to us. Young Robinson looked fit to drop, but his eyes were shining with excitement. He was certainly keen enough. I thought of myself, those first weeks in Malaya, when it had all seemed one big adventure in which I might get shot at but I couldn't possibly get hurt.

We took him forward again so that he could suss out the camp-site with his own eyes.

'You reckon they'll approach from the south?' he asked me.

I nodded.

'So we can either hit them on the way in, or once they're in camp,' he said thoughtfully. I realized he was seeking my opinion.

'Better to hit them once they're in camp,' I said. 'They should be warier on the way in, and if they've any professionalism about them at all they'll lay a snap ambush south of the camp to make sure they weren't trailed. Plus, the camp gives you clearer fields of fire.'

'Yes, yes, of course . . . We'll hit them once they're in camp then. I'll bring up the chaps.' And he slithered back through the undergrowth to his platoon.

'Hear that, Jock?' Chalky whispered. 'He's going to bring up the *chaps*.'

'I feel safer already, so I do,' Paddy said solemnly.

*   *   *

69

The three sections of the Leicesters' platoon were sited in a line to the north of the camp. We didn't dare post a cut-off group to the south of the camp for fear the enemy would spot them on the way in, but we rigged up a trio of claymores there that would catch any survivors who tried to bug out away from our killing group. I posted my team out in the undergrowth to the right of the Leicesters, making the ambush L-shaped – not ideal, but the best we could do in the circumstances – and Robinson also set three of his men to the rear of his own position, facing north, in case the unthinkable happened and the enemy blundered into us from completely the wrong direction. We were set. All we needed now was someone to shoot at.

It's an odd business, waiting in ambush. It proves you can be hyped up to the eyeballs and bored out of your mind at the same time. We lay in position around the camp for the rest of the day, being eaten alive by insects and sucked dry by leeches, the sweat dripping off us in a steady stream. But we had to lie there as still as gravestones, sipping carefully hoarded water and unable to make a brew or even open a tin of food. There was a piece of green string running the length of the killing group which would be tugged the moment the enemy were inside the killing zone, and I had one end of it tied to my wrist. The temptation to sleep was unbearable, and in fact after the first few hours we allowed every other man to grab some gonk. The day trickled past, and finally the sun went down with the shocking abruptness usual in the jungle, and it was night.

Still we lay in position, unmoving and keyed up. It was unlikely, but not impossible, that the enemy would arrive after dark, and I had a couple of Shermuly rocket flares and a pack of miniflares with one already screwed on to the striker, just in case. We also had our spare magazines laid out ready to hand, and of course that bloody string was still attached to me, making sleep difficult. I was scared I would twitch or roll over while I was in the land of nod and set the whole thing off prematurely.

All in all, it was a long night, and I was beginning to think the whole thing had gone for a ball of chalk when the sun finally rose and the jungle sounds took on their accustomed daytime note. The sun rose over a filthy, exhausted and short-tempered bunch of men who were beginning to wonder why they hadn't become grocers or accountants rather than sodding soldiers.

I took a sip of water and rubbed some of the lukewarm liquid into my stinging eyes, when suddenly my wrist was savagely jerked by the green string, which was being frantically yanked up and down. Instantly, my tiredness evaporated.

I got my SLR in the shoulder and sighted on the clearing.

There they were. A file of men in light-green uniforms were trooping into the clearing. They looked as though they had been out in the *ulu* for some time and were obviously bushed. They broke up into knots and pairs and went to their bashas, opening up their light knapsacks and pulling out ponchos.

All this time I was hardly breathing, the slot of the weapon's foresight squarely in the middle of the 'O' of the rear sight, and focused on one enemy who was clearly an officer, as he had a pair of binos and was studying a map.

They were still filing into the camp-site – there seemed to be no end of them. I heard Chalky beside me counting them off in a barely audible whisper and he swore softly as he reached forty. There were a lot more of them than we had thought.

I was impressed by young Robinson. His orders had been that he would be the first to open fire, and so far he was keeping his cool admirably, waiting until every one of the buggers was in the killing zone. But there is such a thing as being too ambitious, and I knew it could only be a matter of time before one of the enemy went for a piss, or the officer set sentries, and then they would walk straight into us.

The crack of the first shot seemed as loud as an artillery round, shattering the peace. One of the enemy went down at once, spinning like a top. And then the firing became general and ear-splitting, and I sent a double-tap into the torso of my officer, then another into the man next to him. After that, all the enemy were on the floor, firing back frantically. I was aware of Chalky's brass winging its way out of the breech of his SLR. I could feel twigs and leaves hitting my back as the enemy fire, hopelessly high, chopped the vegetation above our heads to bits. But mainly my world consisted of the little bisected circle of the rifle sight, and I was banging off rounds in two and threes at anything which moved.

Dead man's click. I was angry with myself – I had miscounted how many rounds I was firing. Shouting 'Magazine!', I changed mags quickly while the rest of the team increased their rate of fire to make up for it.

Sheer bloody pandemonium. The enemy were trying to crawl out of the killing zone, and there was an explosion and screams at their rear as a claymore went off, sending five hundred steel ball-bearings through the air as fast as C4 could propel them. But something else was happening back there, beyond the clearing. Figures were running through the jungle *towards* the ambush.

'Another fucking platoon of them!' Chalky shouted above the mayhem.

More claymores going off, ball-tightening screams, the endless crescendo of firing. Out of the corner of my eye I could see figures and movement off to the right. They were trying to flank us.

'Enemy to your right!' I shouted, and switched aim.

Eight or nine of them came running up at us. I dropped one, and someone else got another. They went to ground then, and began crawling away, pausing every so often to loose off a hail of inaccurate fire at us. I got a grenade, the pin already loosened, and chucked it into the trees. It went off with a flat bang, and two or three men simply got up and ran. We fired, but I don't think we hit any of them.

'Stop!' a voice shouted, shrill with stress and excitement.

Instantly, the firing died out. Silence fell in the clearing, and the smell of cordite hung in the air, along with tendrils of smoke and the sickening stink of charred flesh.

'Watch and shoot! Watch and shoot!' I heard young Robinson shout, and I changed mags again, then lay still and looked out intently at the wrecked enemy camp.

Absolute quiet. My ears were ringing like bells,

though, and I was breathing as hard as if I'd just been sprinting.

Five or six minutes we lay there, and then I saw the clearing group move forward to check the bodies, while the rest of us remained lying still, covering them. Finally they said, 'All clear!' and we emerged cautiously from cover.

There were nineteen dead men lying around us in various states of dismemberment, the flies already congregating about them in black swarms. Altogether, we worked out later, there had been about sixty of the enemy – two platoons or an understrength company. We had been lucky. If the survivors had got their shit together they could have counter-attacked – they had still outnumbered us, even after their losses. But they had buggered off *tout de suite*. Looking at the carnage in the clearing, I can't say I blamed them. They weren't to know they'd been hit by a force of half their number.

Robinson had done well, though it was lucky for him that we'd been posted on the flank of his platoon that the enemy tried to get around. A lesson for the future – guard both flanks, even if it means weakening the killing group. Like I said, we had been lucky.

7

It had been a major coup, and there were pats on the back for all involved, but it didn't change much about our overall mission. We were choppered in from the field and debriefed at the Haunted House, bought a few beers and allowed a good night's sleep, then sent straight back out again into the bush. Major Curtiss promised us a ten-day leave at some point, but he was tolerably vague as to when it might be. We didn't mind too much – we felt we were doing our job and doing it well, and that's enough to keep a man going for a long time.

Krusin finally got his chocolate – or what was left of it – and we spent several days at his village near the border doing the old hearts and minds bit and gagging over a feast of *tapai* and *jarit*. Then it was off to our old stamping grounds on the northern side of Long Pa Sia ridge to see what the enemy had made of his bloody nose there.

The bodies were still there, though there wasn't a lot left of them, and the clearing was full of animal tracks. The local wildlife had been having a regular feast and there were millions of ants underfoot finishing off the clean-up job. The stink was sickening. It didn't seem right, even to us who had killed them, that these men should rot unburied like this. But then again it was a good sign – if the enemy was too frightened to come back and retrieve his dead then we must have made quite an impression. All the same, we found the ambush site surprisingly depressing.

We trekked on up the ridge until we were virtually standing on the border with Kalimantan. It was quite a view from up there. A world of jungle-covered mountains extending as far as the eye could see in all directions, the glint of the River Pa Rava just visible through the canopy here and there to the south, mist hanging in the valleys and the clouds building up overhead into slate anvils, ready for the daily downpour.

'What a fucking country,' Chalky said beside me. 'Why anyone wants to shagging fight over it is beyond me.'

'Like blood from a stone,' I told him. 'A bleeding mystery.'

* * *

Our mission this time was to set up the OP we'd aborted on our previous patrol, and monitor all activity on the ridge, primarily to see what effect the ambush had had on the enemy. So, as the clouds opened and a torrential downpour began, we got out our parangs and began making a hide of sorts. It took us until nightfall, the rain covering the sounds of our chopping, and as the sun winked out we lay in a heavy tangle of undergrowth that was not entirely natural but which looked it and which gave us a good view of the bald-headed top of the ridge. We were all sopping wet, of course, and it was as hot as a Turkish bath. Two men on, two men off. Pete and I took the first stag. He was picking at the scab on his wounded hand until I hissed at him to stop it.

'It itches like a bastard,' he complained.

'That's because it's healing, you numpty. Now leave the bugger alone.'

The leeches were having a sort of blood-fest all over us and we diverted ourselves in the quieter moments by picking them off. The bastards really loved armpits and crutches and in the end we gave up and let them suck away – it was just too disgusting feeling for them in the dark.

We lay there for three days, not moving except to visit the deep hole that served as our latrine. We saw a couple of the locals stroll by with blowpipes over their shoulders and dead monkeys dangling from their free hands, but that was all. If there was any enemy activity going on, it was on their side of the border, not ours. Which was great, of course, because it meant we'd made them think twice about crossing it. But it also made our life boring as hell. That's what three-quarters – or even nine-tenths – of the job was – boredom. Boredom and coming to terms with life in the jungle.

On the fourth day I was on stag with Pete again while Chalky and Paddy slept behind us in the bush. I had the headset of the radio at one ear but there wasn't much traffic and I was damn near dozing off myself. The highlight of the day had been watching a tiny mouse deer about the size of a beagle picking its way across the track without a care in the world.

'Let's catch it,' Pete had whispered mischievously. 'Bet it tastes better than Spam and biscuit.' But the dainty little creature had smelt us on the breeze and taken off in a flash.

I had been given a lot of leeway with this patrol, and it was basically up to my own discretion how long we maintained the OP. As always, professionalism and personal inclination were at odds. I was inclined to jack it in as a waste of time and go roving along the line of the border eastwards – into country we had not yet seen. But I knew that I had to be ultra-sure first that infiltration across the ridge here had ceased. Ideally there would have been two teams in the Bulge, one static and one mobile, but D Squadron just didn't have the manpower.

'I could booby-trap this place,' Pete whispered as the afternoon rain started again and talking became less of a risk under the hissing downpour.

I wiped water out of my eyes, my gaze never leaving the track.

'You what?'

'Rig up a dozen devices – all I need is some C4 and a few flash initiators and detonators. And some wire. I could rig it so the whole area went up if someone came along.'

I thought about it.

'And what if a local walks into it?'

'We'd talk to Krusin first, make sure his people stayed away. They'd do it, Jock. They think you're God Almighty after that ambush.'

I shook my head. 'The OC would never go for it.'

'He might.' Pete was as stubborn as a bloody bulldog once he got an idea into his head. I knew he'd worry it to death if I didn't shut him up.

'Keep your eyes to your front,' I snapped. 'And your mind on the job.'

'It would work, I bet it bloody would,' Pete

grumbled, and then subsided and began staring endlessly out into the rain again.

He had started me thinking, though, the bugger. If he couldn't be in two places at once, this might be the next best thing. As long as some bloody deer didn't set the things off. I wondered if Pete had the necessary expertise for the job.

When our stag ended I tackled him in a barely audible conversation where we murmured into each other's ear like a couple of gossiping teenagers.

'Do you have the know-how for that kind of thing?' I asked him. 'No bullshitting now.'

'Did a course on it, didn't I?'

'Aye, but how much of it stayed in there?' I asked him, and tapped my knuckles against his forehead.

'It'd be dead easy. The tricky bit would be getting the Muruts to stay clear. You know what they're like. They'd be up here trying to nick the detonators or something.'

'Aye . . .' I remembered that when we'd mentioned the idea back at the Haunted House, the OC had actually seemed rather interested, if noncommittal.

'We'll give it a try,' I said at last. 'Make up a list of the stuff you'll need. We'll break up the OP tonight and make for Krusin's village, tell him what's what and see what he says. If he likes the idea too, then we'll get Curtiss on the blower.'

'Krusin will be fine,' Pete said confidently. 'He hates the Indos.'

'Because they disrupt his hunting grounds – which is exactly what we'll be doing with this brainwave of yours. If he says no, then it all goes for a ball of chalk, OK?'

'You're the boss, Jock.'

Krusin didn't seem too enthusiastic when we put the plan to him the next day, but he brightened when I promised him a box of chocolates. While I was discussing things with him, Chalky had his medical kit out and was busy tending to a few of the villagers. The Muruts all had heavy rings hanging from pierced earlobes which over time dragged down the lobe several inches. This was considered a sign of beauty among them. But now, having seen our dinky little earlobes, many of the younger men wanted these drooping bits cut off so they'd look like us. I suppose we should have been flattered, but none of us liked to look as Chalky nonchalantly snipped off the offending bits of flesh and stitched up the wounds. The villagers were lining up for him to do it, their faces lighting up like lamps when they saw the results of the jungle surgery in his little metal hand mirror. Hearts and minds at its most bizarre.

We talked Krusin round in the end and he assembled all the hunters of the village, many of them with bandaged ears, and let them know that the British soldiers were conducting some powerful magic up on the ridge and no one was able to go near it. But there would be presents for everybody to make up for the loss of the hunting area. The crafty bastard had put that last bit in himself, and there was no way we could look cheap and make him retract it.

The only obstacle remaining was the OC. Paddy got him on the radio and I outlined the idea to him. We didn't have to fear being DF'd in those days – that is to say, the enemy didn't have the kit to triangulate radio signals and then hit their sources with an artillery strike. So our conversation was pretty long. What preoccupied Curtiss most was what we were going to do when the trap was set.

'Mike One Zero. We intend patrolling east of this location, and notifying Charlie One if we hear the devices going off. Over.'

I could almost hear the wheels turning in the OC's head. Charlie One was young Robinson's platoon of the Leicesters. He had already been down to the area and knew it well – he was the obvious choice.

Curtiss came back at last.

'Negative, Mike One Zero. Proceed to Echo Charlie's location once devices are in place and guide him back, brief him at the spot. Then your move east is OK. Acknowledge. Over.'

He was going to make us trek all the way up to the Leicesters' camp and back again. I saw Paddy wince slightly as he eavesdropped on the conversation.

'Mike One Zero. Roger. Over.'

'Give me a list of kit needed and I'll arrange resupply by air. Over,' Curtiss told me.

I read him out the list Pete had made up and we arranged a grid where the drop would take place. That was that.

'We've a busy few days ahead of us,' I told Paddy as I gave him back the handset.

'Aye, our fucking feet are going to be walked off us. Pete Conlan and his bloody bright ideas.'

8

We got underway at dawn the next morning. The village of Long Pa Sia, where the Leicesters' company base was, lay some twelve miles to the north. There was a track which ran the whole way, but of course we couldn't use it. We had a hard two- or three-day hike ahead of us, all thanks to Pete's brainwave. He was cheerfully unapologetic, though. He just couldn't wait for the airdrop and the delivery of all those lovely things that went bang. It would be like Christmas come early.

'Why couldn't they have choppered us up there?' Chalky grumbled as we paused for a breather.

'And give the Indos a sign something was up?' I said. 'No way. But look on the bright side – you'll see young Robinson gasping and spluttering all the way back down here.'

'Him? He's keen as anything, that one. Did you see him after the ambush? I thought he was going to shoot his load.'

We moved on. We knew now that Curtiss was going to keep us out in the field for a long time. No more three- or four-day patrols – we were in for the duration. I had already needed to tighten my webbing belt, and I could see the hollows growing under the cheekbones of the rest of the team. We were being stripped down to essentials by the jungle. I wondered how we'd be able to operate efficiently in the long term.

On the second day we ran into a couple of Krusin's people. They were out hunting, north of their usual area since the region around the ridge was effectively off limits to them now. We had a chat and I examined one of their blowpipes. Incredible things. They fire an eight-inch sliver of bamboo over fifty yards with one powerful puff of breath, and the poison on their tips is so toxic that it only needs to graze the skin to kill. The Muruts kept one dart in the pipe and another in their teeth, so they could fire two in a couple of heartbeats. Better than a silenced Browning, if you ask me.

We met no one the rest of the way, for the Bulge was uninhabited except for Krusin's people – at least as far as we could tell. The eastern side of it was still partly unexplored, one of the reasons I was itching to get into it. At this point I and the rest of the team had really got our jungle heads on, and we were as keen to explore new areas of the Bulge for the sake of exploring as we were to run into the enemy. It's not everyone who has a chance in his life – in this century, at any rate – to play at being Livingstone, to travel across country no one's ever set foot in before.

Long Pa Sia village was a thriving place of perhaps two hundred souls. The locals there wore Western clothes over at least parts of their body, and hunted with antiquated shotguns. There were even a couple of ramshackle Land Rovers knocking about. It seemed a veritable metropolis to us, and the Leicesters' camp looked huge and ungainly, built as it was to accommodate over a hundred men. It was a large clearing south of the village itself, surrounded by barbed wire and dotted with sangars made of sandbags and corrugated iron. The local police station, which was no more than a tin shack, was at one side, and there was a space cleared for helis and a wide road leading up north. The Leicesters were resupplied by both road and air. They had even built an officers' mess with a palm-leaf roof, and similar quarters for the men with bunks inside and water piped from a nearby stream by bamboo. Pete's supplies would be choppered in here. I was glad we would be going back south with a platoon of squaddies – they'd be able to help carry them.

This was 1963, and the rest of the British Army was not quite as egalitarian as the SAS. We were not, therefore, invited into the officers' mess for gin and tonics, but instead were shown into the headquarters dugout, a heavily sandbagged structure half underground and lit with stinking Tilly lamps. The Leicesters' OC, Major Martin Wilkinson, was waiting for us there along with his second in command and young Robinson, who immediately shook our hands, filthy though they were.

'Good to have you on board,' Wilkinson told us, as though we were there to assist *him*. He was taken a little aback at our appearance – none of us had shaved or washed in a long time and our presence made the stuffy interior of the dugout more than a little ripe.

'Your OC has informed me of the situation,' he went on, 'and I have agreed to let Lieutenant Robinson liaise with you.'

Bravo, I thought, but only nodded. I saw Paddy and Pete look at each other. Chalky's face had assumed that complete blankness which he always reserved for officers outside the Regiment.

'Your equipment is due to arrive this evening – rather a lot of it, I believe. If you will just have a look at the map here, I'd like you to point out where you are going to place your devices. The operation has been codenamed Viper, by the way . . .'

It was a poor map, as most maps of the Bulge were, but I marked as best I could the location where Pete intended to do his stuff. I'd been thinking about the whole thing on the march north, and the more I turned it over in my mind, the more I was determined that Viper would be sited just on the border, on the southern face of the ridge, not the northern. Less chance of Krusin's people running into it that way. It would mean that we would be trespassing on the soil of Kalimantan ever so slightly, but we could put that down to a navigation error. Curtiss would have disapproved but understood, whereas this man would simply have vetoed it at once. He was a starched-underpants type, so I chose not to tell him.

'Lieutenant Robinson here has orders to set up a platoon hide half a mile north of Viper once it is set up. If the devices go off, he will be on the spot in minutes . . .' Here the OC smiled. 'Won't you, Peter?'

'Rather, sir.'

'However, since I gather from your OC that your team, Sergeant, is planning to bounce off to the east on a long patrol, I intend to keep one of your men here, with Lieutenant Robinson, in case of unforeseen difficulties with Viper. Now, who is your demo expert?'

I could feel my team simmering silently behind me. Did this twat think that just because he outranked us he could break up an SAS team? Even young Robinson had the grace to look embarrassed.

'I'm afraid I can't possibly leave anyone behind, sir,' I said coolly. 'My team must stay together.'

He looked at me, honestly surprised. 'It is not a request, Sergeant. It is an order.'

There aren't many of his kind left in the British Army now, thank Christ. He was the sort who would have been more at home in late-nineteenth-century India, with coolies to order around and drinks on the veranda after sundown. I stood my ground, trying not to let my anger show.

'Sir, we are not in your ORBAT. You have no authority to give orders to my team. We are cooperating because it makes sense, that is all. I take my orders from Major Curtiss in Brunei.'

'Do you, by God? Well, we'll see about that, Sergeant. Corporal Davies!'

A short soldier marched into the dugout. 'Sir?'

'Get me the OC of A Squadron, 22 SAS, in Brunei, and make it quick, man.'

'Yes, sir.'

They had a land-line to the nearest phone cables several miles away, so all Corporal Davies had to do was whirr the handle around a few times on the set and ask the military operator to put him through.

There was an uncomfortable delay during which not a word was said by anybody. We just stood there with the sweat dripping off our noses and sliding down into our eyes. At last Davies handed the handset to Wilkinson. 'Major Curtiss, sir.'

'Yes. Yes, Wilkinson here. Quite. Yes, well the sitrep is as follows, old boy . . .'

It must have been a hundred and twenty degrees inside the dugout, and the four of us were generating a right old stink. Chalky passed round a water bottle and we all had a sip of blood-warm water.

Robinson stared, and then whispered in Davies's ear and the corporal disappeared.

Wilkinson seemed pleased as he came off the telephone, which couldn't mean good news for us. He replaced the handset just as Davies arrived with a tray of four iced lemonades from the officers' mess. Robinson handed them round, earning our gratitude for life.

Wilkinson wiped his brow, smiling slightly.

'That was your OC,' he said. 'He says that on no account is your team to be split up.'

We waited. He looked too smug. There had to be more.

'Therefore, your entire team will be attached to Lieutenant Robinson's platoon until further notice.'

'Is that the word Major Curtiss used, sir – "attached"?' I asked.

'Perhaps not specifically, no,' Wilkinson blustered. 'But his meaning was clear.'

'If we are not attached, then we are not under your orders, sir,' I said coldly. 'In which case Viper will be set up as we see fit, as it is our operation, after all. Lieutenant Robinson?'

'Er, yes, Sergeant.'

'I would be obliged if you and your platoon were at the helipad at 1600 hours, when the drop is due – ready to move out immediately after.'

'Yes, yes, of course,' Robinson said, then looked at his OC. 'That is, sir, if . . .'

'Oh, that's quite all right, Peter. I'm made my point, I believe.' He looked at me. 'We are all on the same side, you know, Sergeant. I know you're disappointed at not getting your little jaunt in the jungle, but it can't be helped. There is a bigger picture, you know.' He smiled benevolently, as a father to an erring son, though he was only a couple of years older than me. I knew that he hated my guts. We had made an enemy here.

'That's all, Sergeant,' he said quietly. 'You are dismissed.'

As we left I heard him say to Robinson, 'Peter, might I have a word with you about the use of officers' mess facilities . . . ?'

We stalked to the helipad. Chalky made as if to throw his SLR on the ground, but it went against too much training. He just stood shaking his head, and muttering softly, 'Cunt.'

Pete was looking guilty as sin.

'Fuck, Jock, I'm sorry about all this. If it wasn't for my stupid idea . . .'

'It's not a stupid idea,' I said, throwing down my bergen and then sitting with it propping up my back, my SLR on my thighs.

'It's a bloody good idea, and should be acted upon. And what's more, that chinless wonder in there is basically right.'

'You're joking,' Paddy said, startled out of his usual taciturnity.

'I'm not. He may be a blue-blooded dinosaur, but he's perfectly right. That's what's so fucking annoying. And it's why Curtiss issued the order he did. Robinson's a good lad, but he's not fit to be let out alone, not yet. He needs someone there to keep him straight – and someone has to stay near Viper who knows how it's set up. It's no good us saying we don't want to play. That just gives the Squadron a bad name.'

'He was an irritating fuck, though, wasn't he?' Chalky said, grinning.

'Chalky, if it weren't for those fucking crowns on his shoulders I'd fill him in, just for being such an arrogant bastard. But there it is. There's nothing we can do but do as we're told.'

Pete was lying on his back with his hands behind his head and his hat down over his eyes. 'We'll have travelled that fucking route down to the ridge so much they'll have to resurface it soon,' he said.

'We should build a road and set up a non-commissioned officers' mess beside Krusin's village,' Chalky said. 'Then get the REMFs back in Brunei to chopper us out some ice and lemonade. Did you taste that stuff? Fucking ice-cold. They know how to live up here.'

'Beer,' said Paddy solemnly. 'A cold Guinness straight up from the cellar with a head on it you could stand a spoon up in.'

'A cold pint of Burton . . .' Pete said dreamily.

'Nah. McEwan's lager, cold enough to make your teeth ache,' I told him.

'Oh stop it,' Chalky groaned. 'I'd give my left

ball for a cold pint of anything. That lemonade just reminded me what *cold* is.'

The chopper arrived bang on schedule, a Wessex filled to the gills with all manner of explosive goodies. Robinson got his platoon to help with the unloading, and it was off again in a matter of minutes, leaving a choking cloud of red dust hanging in its wake. Pete was running around like a blue-arsed fly making a list of everything and arranging with Robinson's platoon sergeant who was to carry what. Claymores by the dozen, pounds of C4, coils of wire and detonator cord, flash initiators and even a box of grenades and some trip flares. It was a pyromaniac's dream.

It took us almost an hour to sort it all out. Pete carried the detonators himself, looking extremely thoughtful as he felt the heat of the box that contained them.

'Problem?' I asked him.

'These fuckers are going to be ultra-sensitive, Jock. Even if you hold them in your hand too long they could go off. We'll have to really get a push on. I'd really rather they didn't go off while they were still in my bergen.'

'Got it,' I said, and began to hustle Robinson and his platoon sergeant.

We were ready to move out fifteen minutes

later, all of us carrying well over the fifty pounds that was considered the limit in the jungle. We didn't know it, of course, but the shit was about to hit the fan in a big way.

9

We were in a hurry, and there wasn't much point in trying to move slowly since we were a crocodile of almost forty heavily laden men. I noted to my dismay that we were indeed creating something of a path as we went, something that could not fail to be noted by any of the enemy who came mooching around. But there was nothing to be done about it. It's a principle that's true for all of Army life. You make do with what you've got, and you never have enough of what you need, be it time, equipment or, in this case, a higher level of jungle skill for the Leicesters who accompanied us. There's a makeshift element to active service that's never quite there when things are quiet. The rules come down, and everyone pitches in. Most of the time, anyway.

We were moving along pretty rapidly, but there wasn't much left in the way of daylight and so we halted before nightfall and set up a platoon harbour. Pete at once dumped the detonators in a nearby stream to keep them cool, and just for the hell of it, he set up three trip flares along the three sides of the harbour, one side to every section of men.

'Just reminding myself how to do it,' he told me with a somewhat shaky grin.

'I thought you had it all off pat,' I retorted.

'I do, I do. But there's no harm in a little refresher before we get down into the border area.'

Trip flares are tricky things to set up, but even trickier to disarm. You have to lie full length on the ground with your face four inches from a pot full of phosphorus and try to get a tiny pin back into an even tinier hole, with the knowledge that the pot will erupt into white flame if you fuck up. Most of the phosphorus goes straight up, so – in theory – your face should be OK and it's just your back that will be showered with the stuff. Not exactly comforting.

But Pete got his three pots set up, with the wires at waist height so they wouldn't be set off by animals, and my team settled down for the soundest sleep they'd had in days, with no stags to take and over thirty men all around us. It made up for the frustration of having to march with them.

It took us three days in all to make our way back down south to the border area. About noon on the third day Chalky was up ahead acting as point for the whole, unwieldy column of sweating men, and I saw him go to ground. I passed on the signal at once and the line went to earth like a load of dominoes. Then I crawled up beside him as he signalled for me personally.

He pointed without a word as I drew abreast of him.

A white shape off in the jungle, square, obviously man-made. It looked for all the world like a 'Keep off the grass' sign. I covered Chalky as he inched forward carefully. He got to within two yards of the thing, and circled it, obviously checking for booby-traps. At last he straightened, and waved me over with a crooked smile.

'What do you think?' he asked. 'We're famous.'

'It *was* a sign, badly whitewashed and scored with black paint. 'Winged Soldiers Beware,' it said.

'I'll be damned.'

'Cute,' Chalky agreed. 'I think we've made an impression.'

'It's clear?' I asked.

'Totally.'

'Then nab it. I have an idea I think Pete might appreciate.'

We returned to the column, the sign under Chalky's arm. The news went down the column

quickly: the enemy were back in the neighbourhood, and they were pissed off. Tired, grimy
men straightened and lifted their eyes from the
heels of the man in front. A new tension took
hold of us all.

I got hold of Lieutenant Robinson.

'Time to switch on, sir. The enemy has been
in this area very recently, and may in fact still
be here. It's another couple of miles to where
we want to site Viper, but I think your platoon
should laager up as soon as we find a decent
location, then you and your signaller and your
section commanders come forward with us to
suss out the area. OK?'

'By all means, Sergeant.'

But by the time we had found a good location
for the new platoon harbour – one the platoon
would be in for some time – and had set
everything up, time was once more against us.
There was no way we'd be able to travel the
required distance tactically and plan the Viper
site before dark, so we knocked it on the head
for the day and decided to set off at dawn.

Everyone was on edge that night, and Pete set
up claymores around the camp perimeter as well
as triple flares, siting the claymores in trees and
angling them so they'd blast across each section's
frontage. The Leicesters were armed with SLRs,

but they had one General Purpose Machine-Gun, also known as a GPMG or gimpy, per section, and they were an excellent piece of kit. They were sited at the corners of the position, and doubled as sentry posts, each man manning one when it was his turn to go on stag. We ran green string all around the position too, with a knot in it at each two-man position, and the lads had dug eighteen-inch shell scrapes.

All in all, we were in pretty good shape, and could have repelled an assault by anything up to a company. We hadn't cleared fields of fire because that would have made us a little too obvious, and the harbour had to be semi-covert if we weren't to frighten the enemy away.

It was a slow night, with no one sleeping much. We were so used to the jungle noises now that they hardly registered, except when there was a change in them. Stand-to saw us all lying down in our scrapes, bergens at our feet, weapons in the shoulder. It was a mist-shrouded dawn, with the sun taking a long time to break through. Dawn in the jungle is ear-splitting. Every creature that's awake seems to get up and scream its head off, but this one was different. The usual mad chorus was subdued. I looked at Chalky, who made a face. Something fishy was going on somewhere.

The Leicesters didn't notice the difference, of course, and as soon as stand-to was over they lit their hexi-stoves and had a brew. It might be a hundred degrees in the shade, with a hundred per cent humidity, but the British soldier still needs his tea.

I thought about cancelling the day's recce and sitting tight in the harbour to see what transpired, but there really wasn't that much to go on – a change in the jungle noises for a few minutes, a feeling of unease – not enough to throw the whole mission out of whack for. So we pulled ourselves together and started out soon after breakfast. My team, Robinson, his signaller, and his three section commanders. We were all heavily laden with Pete's equipment, as he was adamant that he wanted to start setting up Viper that day. As we were already behind schedule, I agreed, and for my sins was weighed down with several claymores, a trip flare, a box of C4 and a coil of det cord which had been hurriedly painted black back at Long Pa Sia. At that moment the whole operation was beginning to seem more trouble than it was worth. The unease of the early morning had not worn off and I was really on edge as we trekked south towards the border, my mood not improved by the racket the Leicesters made as they travelled.

It was early afternoon by the time we reached the border, and I was taking point. Something on the ground caught my eye and I signalled the rest of the patrol to halt, then bent to have a look at it.

We were in primary jungle here, the huge trees creating a twilight with their canopy, and the ground mostly mud. But we were also on the Long Pa Sia ridge itself, and there were rocky outcrops dotted about everywhere which created gaps in the *ulu* and admitted some light. One minute you'd be walking along in semi-darkness, the next you'd step into a patch of blindingly white sunlight.

There were a line of footprints in the mud at my feet. Not bare feet, but booted. Indonesian Army boots. As carefully as though I was stepping round a bomb, I circled the prints, looking for other signs. Some broken twigs. More prints, all heading roughly north-west. At least three men, lightly equipped, judging by the depth of their tracks. With the gear we were now carrying, our own tracks were two inches deep if we stepped in mud, which was why we'd been walking like a bunch of constipated ballerinas all day, trying to avoid it.

I wiped the sweat out of my eyes with my sleeve, and thought about it. The tracks did not contain water, so they had been made after yesterday's rain. They seemed to signify a recce patrol, lightly armed, heading off to the left of the platoon harbour. It was possible they'd noticed the harbour, but then again, maybe not. By the time this patrol had gone out, the harbour had been set up, clearing patrols had gone out and daytime routine had begun. Probably they hadn't noticed it, because we hadn't noticed them, and by the look of things, their fieldcraft was not exactly top-notch.

So I convinced myself, though the unease of the morning was steadily growing. Maybe it was the superstitious Celt in me, but I had a feeling something was going to happen. The enemy were obviously active in the area. Should the whole op be called off?

I was inclined to think so, but then unfortunately I thought of that prick Wilkinson back at Long Pa Sia, and what he would make of it. I decided that we would go ahead regardless.

It was the wrong decision, made for the wrong reasons. There was no one but myself to blame for what was to follow.

10

The day was pretty advanced by the time we got to the border – once again time was not on our side. We'd been ultra-careful, though, on the way down, laying a snap ambush every quarter of a mile or so, and were certain that we had been neither trailed nor noticed. Pete and I left the rest of the patrol in a forward RV and then went on ourselves to the summit of the ridge.

More tracks here. At least a section of men had passed by in the last twenty-four hours, and they had been pretty bloody careless – or confident. The place was a regular thoroughfare, and Pete grinned evilly at me.

'All the tracks are heading north, Jock. We'll get the bastards on the way out.'

'All right. Start thinking about what you're going to do. I'll bring up the others.'

Truth to tell, I was not a happy camper. This did not seem to me to be a healthy place to hang about, though I had to admit it was perfect for

Viper. I brought up the others and we cached all the gear, then took up fire positions as Pete went to work.

He was in his element. He'd even nabbed some epoxy glue from the Leicesters' company stores, and with it he glued moss to the det cord so that it looked like lengths of creeper. He sited claymores in all the surrounding trees, set up trip-wires attached to fragmentation grenades and also to a green smoke grenade. Lastly he planted in the ground the Indo warning sign we'd nabbed further north. He'd scrubbed out the warning and had painted over it in large letters: 'Sabah. Keep Out.' No Indo worth his salt would be able to resist pulling it down, and Pete had attached a trio of C4 charges to its base. He also dug narrow holes with C4 at their bottoms linked to the signpost charges by det cord. The holes were then filled in with stones and tamped down. When they went off they'd spray rocks like shrapnel.

All that was the easy part. The hard part was camouflaging everything so that the area looked completely undisturbed, except for the sign. When it was done it was near sunset, and Pete stood back looking at his creation like an artist studying his canvas. He'd made a detailed grid map of the area, down to the stones and bushes, as he would have to come back and disarm the whole bloody thing if the Indos didn't set it off. I for one was relieved that it was done. It had been a long, tense day just lying there trying to stay alert.

The last thing to do was to take Robinson and his section commanders to the site and point out every trip-wire and charge to them so they could note it for future reference and avoid setting something off themselves if they were ever down there.

By the time that was done, it was pitch-dark, and there was no hope of getting back to the platoon harbour that night, so the nine of us settled down for a night on our tod, about three hundred yards north of Viper. I insisted that four of us be on stag at any one time, which would mean little in the way of sleep, but Robinson agreed. He seemed subdued and excited at the same time to be out here so close to the border with such a small party. For me, there were both too many of us and not enough. Too many to hope to pass unnoticed, not enough to fight our way clear if we got into serious trouble.

As always, I took the stag just before stand-to. Paddy made the usual transmissions both to zero and to Robinson's sergeant back in the harbour, while Robinson's signaller got hold of Long Pa Sia and gave a sitrep to Wilkinson. Most of the men had brew kits with them, but I didn't allow them to use them. We had a cheerless breakfast of water and army biscuits, and got ready to move. It was only two miles back to the harbour, but with so much enemy activity in the area we'd have to take even more than the usual care getting there.

We'd gone about thirty yards when there was a series of tremendous explosions to our rear, in the direction of the ridge. Pete looked at me, and actually laughed.

'You've got to be fucking joking!'

The chain of explosions went on. We could hear the dull thuds of the buried charges going off, and the sharper bangs of the claymores.

'Animals?' I asked.

Pete shook his head firmly. 'No bloody way. It would take a herd of something to set off all the wires.'

We got down in All-Round Defence and listened for ten minutes, still as graven images, a river of leafcutter ants promenading through the midst of us with leaves carried in their jaws like green sails.

No more sounds after the dying echoes of the last explosions. I tapped Chalky's boot with my own and we all got up.

'Mr Robinson,' I told the young officer quietly. 'Could you get your signaller to call up your platoon sergeant and tell him to stay put until he hears from us?'

'Of course,' Robinson said. 'But wouldn't it be better to get the whole platoon down here?'

'Man has a point, Jock,' Chalky murmured.

I shook my head. 'No, Mr Robinson, I'd be obliged if you took your men back to the harbour and remained there until you hear from me. I'm going to take my team down to see what set off Viper.'

He was a good lad, Robinson, and he'd played the dizzy young subaltern bit to perfection. But I could tell I had really pissed him off this time. He was sure I was merely hogging all the glory, and there was mutiny written all over his face. My team didn't look too happy either.

'What's the story, Jock?' Chalky asked.

'I'm not sure. I just don't want thirty-odd men blundering down there. If it was the Indos who set Viper off, then it sounds as though there were quite a few of them. And since we haven't seen any signs of movement from the north, and nor has Mr Robinson's platoon, the odds are that the buggers who set off the charges were moving south to north . . .'

'Reinforcements,' Paddy put in in a low voice.

'Yes. So we still have an unknown number of enemy wandering about the *ulu* round here, and more down by the border feeling very fucking cheesed off – whatever's left of them. We must take a look at Viper, but I want it done with maximum stealth.'

'I see,' Robinson said coldly, looking even more annoyed.

'You sure you're not just being a superstitious old Scot?' Chalky asked me, only half joking.

'Shut up, Chalky. No more discussion. Mr Robinson – will you do as I ask? Rejoin your platoon and await word from us?'

He nodded unwillingly. 'All right, Sergeant. I have the rank but you have the experience. I'll just have to trust you.'

I shook his hand. 'Thanks, boss. Now we'd all best get moving.'

Robinson took his four men off northwards, while I led my team back up to the ridge. We stopped, stock-still, to listen and observe for ten minutes in every thirty. Pete was on point, I came next, with Paddy lugging the radio behind me, and a disgruntled Chalky bringing up the rear.

The feeling that something was going to happen was still there – I just couldn't shake it off, and I began to wonder if my number was up. I've known it to happen – men who have somehow realized that their death is near, and for no rational reason have been right. Chalky was probably correct – it was Celtic mist in my head and nothing more.

It was during one of our listening pauses that I saw them. Nothing more than a flicker of movement, soundless and momentary. I stopped dead, as did the rest of the team behind me.

Nothing more. Perhaps they had caught sight of us too and were waiting as we were. I couldn't even wipe away the sweat that was stinging my eyes.

Their patience wore thin first. I could see one clearly now – he must have been their point man. He had light webbing and an AK and was bareheaded but for a strip of khaki cloth tied around his forehead. He was a small man, very brown, and he was moving with the exaggerated care of a pantomime actor, lifting each boot a clear foot off the ground and looking intently at where it could be set down without making a sound. He was barely twenty yards away, and would inevitably catch sight of me or Pete, who was crouching statue-like a few yards to my left front. It was only a matter of time.

With infinite care, Pete turned to face me, and mouthed the question: 'Open fire?'

I shook my head a fraction. I had to know what was behind this point man – a recce patrol or a whole bloody company.

But I was cutting it very fine.

More men visible now, moving carefully in line but not as carefully as the first. They had more bulky webbing, and one even carried an RPG grenade launcher. I was looking at at least a platoon, and we were in deep shit.

An officer – he had a holstered side-arm and a pair of binos. Him first. I raised the muzzle of the SLR and put three rounds into his chest.

As soon as the first round had cracked out – incredibly, awesomely loud, it seemed – Pete put a double-tap into the enemy's point man.

It took less than a second. I shifted aim and took out the guy with the RPG – two rounds – and then the man next to him – two more.

'Move!' I yelled at Pete.

Chalky and Paddy were putting down a hail of covering fire, Paddy's M16 rattling away on full automatic. Pete and I got up and ran.

All hell had broken loose. There were red tracers zooming through the trees as the enemy finally got their act together and fired back. As I ran, leaves and bits of bark were flying round my ears as 7.62mm rounds smacked into the trees all over the place. The noise was deafening.

I went to ground again, got myself a fire position and shouted, 'Move!' once more.

Chalky and Paddy came running, the radio making Paddy the slower. Pete was on my left, rattling off three- and four-round bursts. I could see the enemy moving – they were closing in on us by fire teams, using the Fire and Manoeuvre SOP. I put down a hail of shots, then changed mags.

I saw Paddy fall.

Chalky turned, grabbed his webbing and dragged him along like a sack. It seemed incredible that he could remain upright in that volume of fire. I saw Paddy moving, and kept firing.

'Move!' I shouted at Pete.

He bugged out. Chalky and Paddy tumbled to the ground beside me. Paddy tore the radio off his back – a round had smacked right into the middle of it, making it useless, but it had saved his life.

'Go, Jock!' Chalky yelled at me.

I went, crawling this time. The enemy still seemed disorganized, but were blasting away at everything in sight. Hundreds of rounds were going down, though most of them were high, fired by frightened and excited men. I crawled for about ten yards – I could see Pete, still to my left, still grimly firing off bursts. I got myself behind a tree, tucked the SLR in my shoulder and shouted, 'Move!' to Chalky and Paddy.

An explosion just behind them. Some bright spark had retrieved and fired the RPG. I could see the orange globe of its back-blast, and put down half a dozen rounds where I thought the firer might be. Someone was shouting orders in Malay, which I could speak, but at that moment I couldn't make out a word.

Chalky and Paddy crawled up. Paddy had the legs of his trousers torn to shreds and the flesh underneath was lacerated and spewing blood, but he got his rifle in the shoulder and started firing back the way he had come.

'Jock!' It was Pete. 'They're off to our left, Jock!'

The bastards had sent a section round our left flank, and Pete was now shifting aim and trying to hold them off.

'Time to leg it,' I told Chalky. 'There's too fucking many of them.'

'You go ahead,' Paddy said calmly. 'I'll hold them up for a while.'

I looked at him. His legs had been sliced to bits and there were thick splinters of wood sticking obscenely out of the muscle. He couldn't walk.

'Jock, Jock – we've got to get the fuck out of here,' Pete shouted, his voice shrill with stress and almost drowned by the din of gunfire. I couldn't see him, but I knew he couldn't hold off an entire section by himself for long. And we were all running low on ammo – I had less than two full mags left.

'Get the fuck out of here, will you?' Paddy said, annoyed.

It was Chalky who finally dragged me away. We crawled a short distance and then got up and ran.

I saw Pete off to my right, fast as a bloody gazelle, and I could hear Chalky puffing behind me. I don't think I've ever moved so fast in my life.

There was still a pandemonium of firing going on behind us, and I heard the crump of the RPG being fired again, but we seemed to have outdistanced the enemy. I halted perhaps three hundred yards further on. Chalky and Pete joined me.

'Where's Paddy?' Pete asked, gasping, his face scarlet. Something had scored open his forehead, and he wiped blood out of his eyes impatiently.

I couldn't speak – only shake my head.

'Oh Christ,' Pete whispered.

'Make for the Leicesters' harbour,' I said at last, surprised that my voice sounded so steady. 'OK?'

They nodded silently. Then the three of us took off again, running like maniacs northwards while the roar of firing gradually grew fainter behind us.

*   *   *

It had once taken us a morning to cover this distance, but we whipped over it now in less than an hour. I guessed that we were only a few hundred yards from the platoon harbour when the new sounds began.

A dull, thudding series of explosions to our rear, which became steadily louder.

'Mortars,' Chalky panted. 'They're walking them down the ridge.'

'Move,' I said.

We ran on. I reckoned they were 81mm jobs, and the Indos were steadily lengthening their range, 'walking' their target grids northwards. If they were deployed anywhere close to the border, they'd be able to range in on the Leicesters' harbour once they located it.

'Are they following, you think?' I asked Pete in another gasping pause.

'Yeah. They're coming on like good 'uns. Jesus, Jock, I think we've run into an entire company of them. It's a half-arsed invasion.'

'That's what I thought. We'll have to get the Leicesters to bug out.'

'Do you think Paddy . . . ?'

'He's dead,' I said brusquely. 'But he bought us time.'

'Shoot and Scoot,' Pete said bitterly.

'We couldn't have done anything else.'

'It's been a bit of a balls-up,' Chalky said quietly, looking at me.

'I know. It was my fault. We should never have been down there in the first place, not with so many signs around.'

'Then we'd just be fighting them up at Long Pa Sia,' Chalky told me. 'At least this way the Leicesters have had some warning. It's not your fault, Jock.'

I had nothing to say to that, so we set off again, slower now, though it was hard not to increase the pace as the mortar rounds drew in steadily closer to our rear. The main thing now was not to get shot by the Leicesters as we entered their harbour. Chalky and I still had our hats, and we turned them inside out so the identifying bands could be seen, but we didn't put much faith in them. As soon as I reckoned we were close enough I shouted, 'British soldiers! Don't shoot – we're coming in!' I did this three or four times before a voice shouted back, 'Identify yourself!' It was just to our front, so my navigation had been all right.

'D Squadron, 22 SAS,' I yelled back. 'There are three of us. Hold your fire!'

We marched in in single file, our rifles held over our heads. Half the weapons in the place were trained on us as we entered the position. I saw young Robinson coming to meet us.

'What the fuck's going on?' he asked, wild-eyed.

11

The way I saw it, we had two priorities. We had to break this Indo incursion, give it a really bloody nose. And we had to go back for Paddy's body.

I reckon my team had taken out at least half of the bastards, and Viper, by the sound of it, had blown away quite a few more, but they had kept on coming. If this was another hit-and-run raid, it was a bloody determined one. Also, it had to be at least company strength. No way could a platoon have taken casualties like that and kept on advancing.

So even Robinson's full platoon would not be a match for it, if and when it appeared. We had to bug out right now and get back to Long Pa Sia, radioing for reinforcements to be sent there as well.

There was only one problem with all this. Lieutenant Robinson wasn't having it.

'We're here in a good defensive position – we

can give a good account of ourselves,' he said. 'If we bug out now they have a chance to catch us on the move, and then we're really in trouble. Better to sit tight and hold them off, wait for reinforcements from Long Pa Sia.'

'They'll be mortaring the arse off you in a few minutes,' I said hotly. We could all hear the explosions come closer down the ridge by the moment. And the infantry would be advancing behind them.

'They've got RPGs and 81mms. You're out-classed, *sir*. We've got to bug out.'

He shook his head stubbornly. 'We stay here. You can take your team back to Long Pa Sia if you wish.'

'It's not the fucking Alamo, you know, sir,' Chalky said quietly. 'Jock is making a good point. And reinforcements could take thirty-six hours to arrive – they can't set choppers down in the middle of a fire-fight. We'd be entirely on our own.'

'I've made my decision. I'll call up the OC and see what he thinks,' Robinson said. 'If he orders us to pull out, we'll pull out.'

That was that then. I just knew that stuffed shirt Wilkinson would keep this platoon here. I turned away.

'What about us, Jock?' Pete asked. He seemed a little shocked by the day's events. 'Do we stay?'

'These buggers will need all the help they can get,' I told him. 'We've no comms either, and we're almost out of ammo. If they stay, then so do we.'

'And we'll even a few scores too,' Chalky added darkly.

Sure enough, Robinson's OC told him to stay put, and promised that reinforcements would be rushed to him as soon as practicable. I think he had visions of a gong for himself. In the harbour, meanwhile, we made ready to receive an attack, deepening the shell scrapes and setting out every claymore we had. All the time the mortar fire continued, until we were barely aware of it any more.

I kept thinking of Paddy, the way we had left him. We had been following SOPs, sure, but it still felt bad. I wondered if there could perhaps be some way he might have survived, and angrily told myself to wake up. He was dead, and we had to get on with the job in hand. That was all there was to it. For the moment anyway.

The Leicesters doled out a few mags of ammo for us, but they had no 5.56mm rounds for the M16, so Pete would have to make do with what he had, plus his Browning. All in all, we were in fairly good shape to receive an attack, I thought, but it all depended on how the Indos wanted to play it. If they stood off and hit us with the 81mms for any length of time, our prospects would not be rosy – the shell scrapes had been deepened to waist height, but would still offer less than adequate protection against a determined bombardment. And there were so damn *many* of the fuckers.

I was still a little shaken up by the situation we'd just been in, and by Paddy. Any prick who tells you he can go through a fire-fight and waltz out the other end without a tremor is a liar. The whole thing leaves you feeling limp as a fucking wet rag, especially if you've lost a mate.

I also managed to talk to Major Curtiss on the Leicesters' radio. Once he had found out that he'd lost a man, he'd flown down to Long Pa Sia at once. He was pretty curt over the air, merely ordering my team to remain with Robinson's platoon, wherever it decided to be. With the jungle below the village swarming with the enemy, this was no time for three men to try and make it through alone. I could tell he was seething, though, both because he had lost a bloke and because Wilkinson was the local commander he had to deal with.

I had just come off the radio when one of the GPMGs opened up at the southern corner of the harbour.

'Stand to!' Robinson yelled unnecessarily.

Everyone was already in their scrapes behind their weapons.

The gimpy fell silent again. Robinson and I beetled over to the position, crawling up beside the gunner.

'What were you firing at?' I hissed at the young man before Robinson could open his mouth.

'Thought I saw movement . . . Sergeant.'

'Where?'

'See the big tree with the creepers? One knuckle right of that.'

We all lay still, watching. Not a thing.

'Could have been a pig or snake or something,' Robinson said unhappily.

'Could have been,' I answered irritably. I turned to the gunner. 'You don't open up unless you have a clear target – got it?'

'Yes, Sergeant.'

'If the Indos didn't know our location before, they fucking do now. Mr Robinson, I suggest you get back to platoon headquarters . . .' I paused. The mortaring to the south had stopped.

'Shit,' I said.

'What is it, Sergeant?' Robinson wanted to know. He was hacked off that I had chewed out one of his men in front of him, and I suppose he was right to be, but I really didn't care at that moment.

'They're shifting aim,' I said softly. 'Everyone get your heads down in your scrapes – *now*.'

I had barely scrambled back to the fetid hole I shared with Pete and Chalky when we all heard the distinctive hollow pops of the mortar rounds.

'Take cover!' some idiot yelled.

Three rounds fell perhaps thirty yards south of the harbour – thump . . . thump . . . thump. Wood splinters, leaves and all sorts of crap went hurtling through the air. Then silence again for a second.

'Fuckers missed us,' I heard one of the squaddies gloat.

'Keep your fucking head down!' I yelled at him.

The second salvo came swooping in, to the north of us this time – three more shells that showered the men in the scrapes with dirt.

'They've got us bracketed,' Chalky said grimly. 'Now the fun'll start.'

'They must have a forward observer out there somewhere calling in the ranges,' I said. 'That, or they're fucking clairvoyant.'

More rounds came hurtling down, and this time they had them right where they wanted them. They landed square in the middle of us with deafening booms. I felt all sorts of shit land on the back of my neck as I cowered in the shallow trench. A man began screaming on the other side of the position.

'Some poor bugger's copped it,' Chalky said, spitting mud out of his mouth. 'Must go, gents. Duty calls.'

'You stay put . . .' I ordered him.

'With respect, Jock – go fuck yourself,'

He set off at a crouch with his rifle in one hand and his medic kit in the other.

Another salvo. Their mortarmen were shit hot, I'll give them that. I saw Chalky dive into the nearest trench like a rabbit going down a hole, just as three more rounds came down in our midst.

We were both lucky and unlucky with the mortars. The ground was so soft that they buried themselves deep in it before exploding, and so much of their force was absorbed. On the other hand, there were trees all around that, when hit by the high explosive, produced showers of splinters like some kind of wooden shrapnel. The bloke Chalky was trying to treat had had his shoulder ripped open by a piece of tree, and was spraying blood like it was going out of fashion. I could hear young Robinson sending a contact report and, to give him credit, he was almost coherent.

'They don't fucking pay us enough,' Pete grumbled, and I actually laughed.

The mortaring went on for another fifteen minutes or so, by my watch, though I could have sworn it was more like an hour. Two more men were hit, and Chalky darted back and forth between salvoes to treat them. Flesh wounds, as far as I could make out – spectacular but not life-threatening. I think Chalky's clipping and stitching hurt them more than the injuries themselves.

And then it stopped.

'Oh fuck,' Pete murmured. 'Here we go.'

The mortaring had silenced the jungle for miles around, and the quiet was eerie. I actually thought for a second that I'd gone deaf, until someone coughed, shattering the stillness.

'Look to your front,' I heard Robinson's platoon sergeant say calmly.

'I feel like the bloody cowboy in the wagon train waiting for the Indians to ride up,' Pete muttered to me, and I nodded. It went against the grain of all our training to just sit and wait for the enemy.

A loud bang as one of the claymores went off, and someone out in the jungle screamed. More explosions. They were moving in on all three sides of the harbour at once.

An absolute storm of gunfire opened up on all sides. In the shadow under the trees I could see dozens of muzzle flashes twinkling, and then the flare of an RPG being fired. I don't know where the grenade landed. Pete and I didn't fire a shot, as we were in the middle of the position. We'd tackle any breakthrough or strengthen any section that seemed to be weakening. The Leicesters were answering in kind, and I could see the shining snake of links disappearing into the breeches of the gimpies as the three gunners poured it on. There didn't seem to be many fire-control orders, but there were no panicky fire-the-whole-fucking-magazine-as-fast-as-you-can incidents either. From what I could see, the men on the perimeter were aiming carefully at the muzzle flashes of the enemy and sending out three or four rounds at a time.

The firing built up to a crescendo, and then began to die away. A few isolated shots continued to ring out until Robinson shouted, 'Cease fire! Watch and shoot, watch and shoot!'

Silence again, but I thought I could hear movement off in the trees. They had been feeling us out. Now they were setting themselves up for the real attack.

'I used to think these buggers were a load of wank,' Pete told me quietly. 'Forgive me for saying so, but they're actually pretty bloody good.'

'The Indos, you mean.'

'Yes. You think I was talking about the Leicesters?'

I didn't answer, too intent on the shadowy jungle beyond the perimeter. I wished now that we had been less concerned with being sneaky-beaky and had cleared proper fields of fire.

Chalky came sliding into our trench, his hands black with blood. 'Nice day for it,' he observed.

'What's the score?' I asked him.

'Three from the mortars – scratches. Two more bullet wounds, one a bit nasty, got it in the lung. Sounds like a harmonica full of spit.'

'Charming,' Pete said.

'Think they'll come again, Jock?' Chalky asked me.

'Is the Pope a Catholic?'

We huddled in our filthy little hole in the ground. We could hear orders being shouted in Malay way off in the forest, too far for me to catch what they were. Everyone seemed oddly calm. Pete even took the time to pull through the barrel of his M16.

'You know what this fucker is like if it gets dirty,' he explained as he put the weapon back together again under our incredulous eyes.

'American-made rubbish. Go for the good old SLR next time,' Chalky advised him.

'It's Belgian,' I told him.

All this time we were conversing in whispers, as if afraid of being overheard, and our eyes never left the wall of jungle all around us.

'Wish they'd get a fucking move on,' Pete groused. 'I'm dying for a piss.'

It started behind us. First the gimpy opened up, making us jump out of our skins, and then firing became general. They were assaulting the eastern side of the harbour while a couple of sections kept up a desultory fire on the rest of us.

Two more claymores went off, spraying showers of steel ball-bearings across the front of the eastern section. The RPG opened up, but the twat was still firing high. I could see them now – small groups of men who got up out of the vegetation and dashed forward five yards, then went to ground again. Fire and Manoeuvre, just like they teach it at Brecon. They were brave men, but as they got closer to the harbour the fire they received pinned them down. They began to crawl along the ground by sections, pausing to fire every now and then, while behind them at least a platoon of their comrades kept a withering rattle of automatic fire raining down on Robinson's positions.

They were dying now, in ones and twos. We could hear their wounded men shrieking for help while their NCOs shouted at them to keep moving. But they could not get any closer. Barely thirty yards separated them from the trenches of Robinson's men, but that thirty yards was a fearsome killing zone. The attack died out, the firing slackened again. Their wounded could not be rescued, and remained screaming in the mud or pulled themselves behind the shelter of trees. All around, their comrades continued to shoot into the harbour, but it was a harassing fire, no more, as if they just wanted to remind us that they were still there.

'That was a bit fucking close,' Chalky said. 'They really want our arse in a basket, don't they?'

'Some time soon they'll figure out how to use their numbers all at once,' I said.

Pete was looking up into the canopy overhead, squinting at the chinks of sunlight up there that somehow made it through the trees.

'Still a fair bit of daylight left,' he pointed out. 'I'm not looking forward to spending the night here.'

I nodded. We'd never be able to maintain the integrity of the perimeter at night, not now the claymores had all been fired. Soon it would become a race against time. What would happen first? Would we be overrun or would reinforcements arrive like the cavalry in a B Western?

Lieutenant Robinson came crawling into our trench while rounds continued to crack overhead.

He looked shattered, but then I suppose we all did.

'Everyone all right?' he asked in his best officer-like manner.

'In the pink, sir,' Chalky told him.

'I've just been on the radio to Long Pa Sia,' Robinson said. 'The two other platoons of the company are ready to move, and reinforcements are being flown in there from Sarawak – Gurkhas. Major Wilkinson is waiting for the Gurkhas to arrive before he sets out to relieve us.'

'What?' I couldn't believe my ears.

'Do you mean he's still sitting at Long Pa Sia with his thumb up his bum?' Pete exploded.

'That's enough, Private,' Robinson said.

'Christ Almighty,' I said, shaking my head.

'Intelligence suggests,' Robinson went on in a strained tone, 'that there may be as many as a battalion of the enemy in the area, and that they are keeping us here as . . .'

'Bait,' I finished for him.

'Exactly.'

'I'd like to know where he gets his intelligence,' Pete growled. 'I thought *we* were supposed to provide him with it.'

'Shut up, Pete,' I said, and turned to Robinson. 'So we're to hold on here like fucking Beau Geste until he gets enough troops together to confront this hypothetical enemy battalion.'

'That's about the size of it, Sergeant.'

'Do you believe there's an entire battalion out there, Lieutenant?'

He wouldn't meet my eyes. 'If this is just a holding action, they're being awfully intense about it. I don't know, Sergeant. When it comes down to it, I just obey orders, the same as you.'

'Well, thanks for putting us in the picture. How is the platoon holding out?'

'Five casualties, one serious. We've about four mags left per man and five hundred link for each of the gimpies.'

'So we can hold off perhaps two more attacks like the last one?'

'I think so.'

'We're not going to last until the rest of your company gets here, you know that, sir,' Chalky said quietly. 'This is not just a holding action – these fuckers are out to annihilate us. I reckon they took eight or nine casualties in that last attack. We've really pissed them off.'

'What do you suggest?' Robinson asked, angry now. 'That we make a run for it with an entire enemy company at our heels?'

'How mobile are the wounded?' I asked him.

'All walking, except for Peterson, the lung shot. He's a stretcher case.'

I thought about it, but any way I looked at it, it seemed we were really in the poo. A fighting withdrawal is the hardest of all military manoeuvres, and when the unit withdrawing is outnumbered and virtually surrounded, well, it becomes something of a joke.

'Lieutenant Robinson is right,' I said heavily at last. 'There's no way we can get out of here under our own steam. We've no choice but to sit tight and hold on until the cavalry arrive.'

'Terrific,' Pete snarled. Chalky and I looked at each other. Pete had been badly affected by Paddy's death. The two of them had been through Selection together and were much of an age. I hoped he wasn't going to crack up on us.

'Better settle in for the night then,' Chalky said with a shrug.

12

We'd pissed them off all right. The mortaring began again a few minutes later, and some of the men on the perimeter opened up on figures they saw moving back through the dense brush. They were pulling back to give their support weapons a free hand. There was nothing for it but to get our heads down and wait out the barrage.

I reckoned they had a single section of 81mms, with one crew better trained than the other. The salvoes came down almost in threes, as before, but the timing was ragged, so it was probably two tubes, with one firing much faster than the other.

We would lie there with dirt in our mouths, and two rounds would land almost together, then a third would hit about five seconds later. The explosions were knocking all kinds of shit out of the trees, and there was actually a burst of laughter from one side of the harbour as some unfortunate found a dazed snake in his lap. It had been blasted there from somewhere up in the canopy.

'How far away do you figure those tubes are?' I asked Chalky. He had been a corporal in a support company before he earned his wings.

'Could be anything up to five miles,' he told me. 'But I think they're closer. They're absolutely spot on, see. I'd be surprised if they're more than two miles away . . . What's on your mind, Jock?'

'Something bloody silly,' I said absently.

The mortars had to be taken out, or they'd quickly wear us down to the point where the enemy would be able to virtually stroll over the position. Two tubes – say, eight men. I checked the mags on my SLR and the Browning pistol.

'Don't start getting all gung-ho on me now,' Chalky warned.

I shook my head. 'I'm going to have a bash at silencing those two tubes.'

'Not on your own, you're not.'

I lowered my voice so Pete wouldn't hear. 'You're the medic – you're needed here. And Pete has the jitters. I'm going for it.'

'Don't be a bloody fool, Jock.'

'Stay put and shut it.' I crawled out of the shallow trench, slithered over to Robinson and told him what was on my mind. He looked incredulous, but nodded, knowing as well as I did that the attrition being caused by the enemy mortars could not be suffered much longer. Now that they had our coordinates, they'd be able to keep firing all night if they wanted. We'd be lucky if we had a dozen effectives left by morning.

It was arranged in five minutes. I crawled over to the southern side of the perimeter and waited there like a sprinter ready for the starting pistol. But my starting pistol took the form of a furious blast of fire which erupted all along the harbour perimeter. The south-facing section fired slightly high, and I crawled out of the position with tracer arcing a few feet over my head. The SLR was strapped to my back and I had the Browning cocked in my right fist. I'd gone perhaps thirty yards when I saw someone ahead of me, and the muzzle of a rifle come up, slowed by surprise. I put three rounds into the bloke's head, then kept going, hauling myself up to his corpse. More of the fuckers. They were all around me. I began to wish I'd listened to Chalky. Brainwave time. I pulled the tunic off the man I'd killed and slipped it on, holstered the pistol and took his AK too. Then I went on south at a crouching run.

Maybe they thought I was one of their own doing a runner. Someone shouted at me in Malay. '*Orders*,' I yelled back in the same language. It made them hesitate just long enough for me to get another ten yards. Then they opened up, not having been born yesterday. I emptied the AK at a couple who were closest, threw it away and ran like fuck.

That horrible crawling feeling between my shoulder-blades, my back feeling as large as the side of a house. What with the Leicesters' covering fire, and another salvo from the mortars, I couldn't distinguish the shots being fired at me from the rest, but there were leaves and bits of twigs flying in a halo all around me. I've never run so fast in all my life.

I reckon I covered a good half a mile before I paused. It was quieter now. They were bound to send out a section after me, but I had a few minutes' grace while they got their shit together.

Trouble was, I was utterly shattered. This was beginning to make Selection look like a picnic in the Welsh hills. My legs were like rubber and I was close to hyperventilating, while the inside of my mouth was as foul as a kid's sandpit. Bad ju-ju, as some of the old Mau Mau sweats used to say.

I got up and kept going, unslinging the SLR. It was an effort to even keep the butt of it in my shoulder. I paused a few times to listen and watch, but for the moment I seemed to have outdistanced any pursuit. After another half a mile or so, though, I heard another sound which brought me up short. It was the hollow *thoom* of a shell leaving a mortar tube.

I listened again. There they were. *Thoom thoom*. Off ahead of me somewhere.

I clicked up the rear sight of the SLR – it had been snapped down in my gold-medal sprint through the jungle. Time to start switching on. I started forward again, slow this time, doing it properly. I could hear my heartbeat shushing back and forth out of my open mouth. It seemed to me to be nearly as loud as the jungle noises, and for a daft second I wondered if it would give me away.

I could hear the snap of orders now, in addition to the sound of the shells leaving the tubes. Not far. After they hit us the first time they must have relocated the mortars farther north. It must have half killed them, hauling the tubes and heavy base plates through the jungle. These blokes weren't half bad.

Thoom thoom – getting louder as I drew closer. I wiped sweat out of my eyes as slowly as if I was polishing old porcelain. I'd lost my hat somewhere below the harbour and the salt was stinging my eyes like a bastard. Nearly there.

I saw them. They hadn't cammed up, knowing the Brits would never use air power on them, and trusting in their comrades farther north to keep the enemy clear. They'd slashed themselves a little clearing, and the base plates of the two mortars were already a foot deep in the mud of the forest floor, sinking half an inch with every round fired. Silly sods should have made a bed of branches and logs for them, but I suppose they'd been in a hurry.

Six men. They were understrength, and their NCO was mucking in along with the rest, sighting each tube himself and loading one – the one that Chalky reckoned had the high rate of fire – with his own hands. The rest of his men had the awkward look of untrained or badly trained soldiers, probably drafted in from a rifle company. He was the only real mortarman among them. Him first.

I rehearsed mentally what I would do, putting everything else out of my mind. Then I straightened the pin on a grenade – try to pull one of those with your teeth and you'll need dentures, no matter how they do it in the films – and laid out my spare mags beside me.

Grenade first. I tossed it in among them and in the next instant had the sights of the SLR on them again. The NCO saw the grenade, opened his mouth to shout, but never made it, because I'd put three rounds into him. He went down and the grenade went off at almost the same moment. That put them all on the floor, some of them screaming, others scrambling for side-arms.

I potted another one with a couple of rounds to the head and neck. They were firing back wildly now, but still hadn't quite sussed out where I was. I changed fire position and slotted another guy who was idiot enough to get up and run for it. Then the fire coming down around me grew heavier, and I crawled backwards behind a tree.

The enemy fire halted. They'd been firing on full automatic, and the silly sods had all run out of ammo at the same time. I got up on my knees, chanced a look and shot one who was fumbling with his spare magazines. Then I ducked down again, grabbed my own mags and moved off to my left. They were still firing at where I had been, not where I was. I threw in another grenade, heard the flat crump as it went off, then popped my head up for another look. Two men were bugging out, crashing through the vegetation as they went. I fired off the rest of the magazine at them, but missed, threw myself down again and changed mags.

Men shouting both to my front and my rear. Time to clear off, but in which direction? I knew I was facing roughly west, and the harbour was to my right, but I didn't fancy my chances of trying to get back through the enemy, not now they'd been stirred up. I went off to my left instead, crawling through the mud and ducking my face to the ground as the undergrowth ripped at my back and clawed at my webbing. It was *belukar* here, which suited me fine. I found a low tunnel through the thick vegetation, which was scarred by pig trails, and squirmed along it. The enemy were all over the place now, doing a passable headless-chicken imitation. These men were not as well trained as the unit which was besieging Robinson's platoon. They were firing at anything and everything, just asking for a blue-on-blue. I wormed my way into a low depression overhung by a riot of brush and lay still, trying to get my breath back.

I had two full magazines left, forty rounds, plus three mags for the Browning, and a smoke grenade. I treated myself to a sip of foul, rubbery water from my water bottle and lay back to await events.

The grenades had been pretty much on target, so there was a good chance they had fucked up the optics of the mortars and thrown them off whack. Plus, I'd killed their expert. They would get the things firing again, but I doubted if they'd be able to do it with any accuracy, and the possibility of hitting their own men might convince them they should knock it on the head altogether. Mission accomplished, I thought. Now to problem number two – how to keep myself in one piece and make it back to the others. No chance of moving out while it was still daylight and the enemy was still running about all over the place. I'd have to wait until after dark, which was only a few hours away. I had an escape compass sewn into the lapel of my shirt – I'd left the prismatic with Chalky, like an idiot. I ripped it out now and studied it carefully, figuring I'd have to make a wide dog-leg to get clear of this area before I could start heading north again.

It was an unpleasant time, to say the least. The insects and leeches were feasting on me in their hundreds, but I had to remain motionless, because the Indos were thrashing through the brush on all sides, sometimes coming as close as ten yards away. I was beginning to think my number was up, but they moved away as it drew on to nightfall, and I was left alone.

No more firing – mortars or small arms. I wondered if they had given up on assaulting the Leicesters, or were preparing for one last big attack. The Leicesters would never be able to hold their own against a massed night assault, but on the other hand, command and control would be a complete fucking nightmare for the enemy company commander. It was a toss-up.

Pitch-darkness. Time to move.

Ever so slowly, I got on to my hands and knees and began inching out of the hollow. I'd go two yards, then pause to listen. I was feeling my way, literally, with one hand padding the air in front of my face and slowly moving aside low branches and leaves. Then I had a lucky break.

Steady rain began rattling down on the canopy with the sudden ferocity of the tropics. The noise of it seemed deafening, a continuous roar. It was both a blessing and a curse, as it would cover all sounds – not only those I made, but also those made by the enemy.

I stood up and began moving more rapidly. No question of covering my tracks in the dark, so I moved as carefully as possible. My eyes felt as wide as dinner plates.

Another sixty paces, and I stopped. In that world of ragged shadows and pouring water, pools of utter blackness, I saw a tiny blink of orange light that lasted only a moment and then was gone. I stood immobile, waiting, and after a few seconds it came again, this time the light moving in a short arc. I was watching a man smoking, the tip of the cigarette sheltered by his cupped hand.

I remained completely still. A sentry – it had to be. So there was an enemy position ahead.

I turned to my right and began slowly to walk away, if you can call what I was doing walking. I must have been moving at about fifty yards an hour.

Then I heard a low voice talking. I froze again, heart hammering like it was going to pound out of my chest. I looked all around, and could just make out something large and angular which shone with the rain. Slight movement below it, and two voices murmuring now, the rain almost drowning them out.

A basha formed by a poncho suspended between two trees, with two men under it. Christ, I was in the middle of the enemy camp.

13

For a second, I have to admit, I was close to chucking my teddy bear away. I froze like a deer caught in headlights, and it was only with the greatest effort that I could make myself slowly look around in the rainswept darkness.

More bashas. I was in the midst of a circle of them, a platoon or company harbour. I'm fucked, I thought.

I sank to a crouch with infinite slowness, rain dripping in my eyes, the grip of the SLR slimy with sweat in my palm.

They had no idea I was anywhere near. They'd just basha'd up for the night as if they hadn't a care in the world. A platoon of them, I reckoned, probably under orders to protect the mortars from any more mischief. While I'd been hiding in the brush, they'd been setting up camp all around me. I was furious with myself for getting caught like this, but if I looked at it realistically, there wasn't a lot else I could have done.

So now what?

I couldn't just walk out through them – they were well into night routine now, and no one was moving. They'd blow me away at once.

Then it occurred to me. The sentries would have to be relieved at some point. In a platoon harbour you usually have three, one to each side. I'd make a break for it when they changed.

No soldier in any army ever remains on stag for more than a couple of hours at night – there are limits to how long a man can remain alert in the dark. So there was nothing for it but to wait.

The rain eased off after a while, and the jungle quietened. It was as humid as a Turkish bath, and the mossies were swarming in tiny, maddening clouds around my eyes and mouth. I drew them in whenever I breathed. I picked a leech off my cheek. The bastards were all over me, but they were a fact of life now, hardly even an irritation any more. The minutes dragged by.

I thought of home, of Hereford, of the rest of the lads in D Squadron. I thought of Paddy, his body still unburied down on Long Pa Sia ridge. Unfinished business. I found myself wondering if Pete would straighten himself out. I'd seen it before, the mixture of anger and baffled grief at the death of a mate. The first is always the hardest, whereas all the crap people talk about killing your first man is just that – crap. It had never bothered me, anyway. No, it was losing a friend that was hard to take. The enemy were there to be killed, not to lose sleep over.

Back in the real world, there was movement around me, men talking in low voices. The sentries were being relieved. Time to move.

These blokes really were a load of rubbish. The sentry is supposed to stay in place until his relief comes to him. He doesn't leave his post, even if his replacement is late. But these jokers were wandering in from their posts and chatting to the guys who were about to relieve them. Still, it was better for me this way.

I got up, and began to amble out of the position as if I hadn't a care in the bloody world. I actually nudged a sleeping soldier by accident and heard him grunt a curse, but made myself keep going. To freeze now would give the game away. I murmured an apology in Malay and kept going. Alice in fucking Wonderland.

Ten feet, twenty feet, thirty feet. I'd checked my direction with my little button compass, squinting at the tiny luminous face in the darkness. I was heading north. I fought an urge to run.

I was outside their perimeter now, and slowed, moving a couple of yards every few minutes. Don't rush it, I told myself. *Feel* your way through the tangle of invisible creepers, ferns and branches.

Thirty yards perhaps. My arms were quivering with strain and the weight of the SLR. Sweat was dripping off the end of my nose, sliding through my eyebrows, but I didn't dare pause to wipe it away.

Fifty yards. A hundred. They hadn't even set out trip flares.

Famous last words. I'd been getting almost cocky. A tug at my ankle, and I pulled back my leg at once. Too late. A hissing sound, and then a huge, unbelievable explosion of light off to my right.

Night vision shot to shit in a hundredth of a second, and immediately the awesomely loud explosion of automatic fire.

I had thrown myself through the air to my left, away from the exploding flare. I hit the ground rolling, blind as a bat, then crawled on furiously while behind me the entire enemy perimeter erupted with gunfire, the pitch-dark night lit up with muzzle flashes, the trip flare burning bright as a sun in the jungle. Stupid, *stupid* bastard.

Rounds clipping the bushes around me. I couldn't see a damn thing – my sight was still blazing with after-images. But I kept moving. No point in returning fire – the muzzle flash would only give me away. I was crawling with the last of my strength, the breath sobbing in and out of my throat thick and heavy as treacle.

For maybe fifteen minutes I crawled frantically, then forced myself to halt and take stock.

The gunfire behind me had died down. It was possible they thought the trip flare had been set off by some animal. They'd have to send a couple of men or a fire team to check it out, so they had stopped firing. They'd never catch me in the darkness. I was out, free, away.

I took out my water bottle and found that a bullet had gone clean through it – I could put my finger in the hole. I had a bit of a shake then, and actually had to stop myself from laughing out loud. Christ Almighty, it had been close. One for the scrapbook, without a doubt.

I pulled myself together. Not too far now to Robinson's position, but there was half the Indonesian Army still in between. Best to sit tight for a while. That flare had unnerved me, and my night vision was taking a long time to return. I crawled under some bushes and lay still, like a fox the hounds had passed by. I was desperately thirsty, but my perforated water bottle was empty. I felt, in a phrase my old colour-sergeant used to employ, like three pounds of shit stuffed in a two-pound bag. The adrenalin was still rocketing through me, but I felt washed out as an old tea bag. A six-year-old with a water-pistol could have taken me prisoner. Damned if I didn't doze off.

When I woke from a sleep I had never meant to take, it was morning. I lay there completely disorientated for a second, then I switched on. I must have slept for five or six hours. The jungle was full of mist and hanging water vapour. If a brontosaurus had come lumbering up out of the fog, I wouldn't have been surprised.

There were the usual forest noises, but a little subdued perhaps by the pandemonium of the last few days. I had a careful look around, then rose to my feet. No sign of the enemy, or anyone else for that matter. I checked my little compass, then began picking my way northwards. The rest had done me good, and I felt almost fresh, if horribly thirsty. And I think the leeches had got all but a pint or two of my blood in the night.

I seemed to have been in the jungle for ever. I was part of it now, and to move as carefully as a hunted animal seemed wholly natural. I no longer noticed the heat, the crushing humidity or the million and one parasites which infested me. That's why I saw them before they saw me.

A line of enemy soldiers moving north to south, like a series of beaters out to flush pheasant. They were sixty yards ahead, moving quietly but not quietly enough. Little, brown-faced men who looked fresh and alert – and who carried SLRs.

I paused. A wild notion of charging them and going down fighting had come to me, but now I noticed the differences. British Army jungle fatigues, bush hats. Farther back, a European face – an officer with his radio operator tramping along behind him. Gurkhas.

I felt like shouting, like running forward waving my arms, but then I got a grip on myself. I thought about it for a few minutes while the line drew closer. The last thing I wanted, after everything I had survived, was to be potted by Johnny Gurkha. It would be such a bloody embarrassment.

But what was I to do? They were thirty yards away now, two platoons abreast and a third in reserve. A whole bloody company of them.

'Hey there!' I shouted at last, feeling like an idiot.

'Sergeant Ross, 22 SAS. Don't shoot!'

They'd gone to ground at the sound of my voice, rifles pointing menacingly in my direction. I swore, then shouted again, 'This is Jock Ross, D Squadron, 22 SAS. Don't shoot, you bastards! I'm going to stand up!'

I did so, holding my SLR out at arm's length and feeling about as scared as I had been in the middle of the enemy camp the night before.

'Jock, you Scotch bastard!' a voice said. 'We thought we'd got rid of you at last!'

And I found myself looking into Chalky's filthy, grinning face.

14

The beer was so cold it made my throat ache. They'd had it in the freezer, so that the bottom quarter had frozen solid, though it didn't take long to thaw. I threw back another gulp, closing my eyes as the stuff went down. Coldness. I'd almost forgotten what it was like.

A bar in Brunei, just a few streets down from the Haunted House. Chalky, Pete and I were sat there with our elbows planted on the bar top and a little Dyak in an awesomely tasteless shirt grinning opposite us. We'd been there an hour and had five bottles each. It was his lucky day.

Pete finally came up for air. Wiping his mouth, he sighed and waggled the neck of his empty bottle. Another was plopped down in front of him and he stared at it with a mixture of ecstasy and ruefulness.

'They put formaldehyde in it, you know,' he said to no one in particular. 'Only thing that'll keep it in this heat.'

'Don't give a fuck,' Chalky retorted, downing another one.

A cloud of dust rose from the street and drifted in the open front of the bar. I twisted on the stool and looked out at the crowded street. Water-buffalo-drawn carts, bicycles, mopeds, the odd ancient car tooting its way through the throng. The noise and the crowds still made me a little uneasy after the jungle, and when a car backfired I hopped on the stool like a frog.

'Still wound up,' Chalky observed.

'Tight as a nun's knickers,' I admitted. 'Doesn't seem real somehow.'

'What? This, or the jungle?'

'That's just it. I don't know.'

We'd just had the bloodiest tour of any unit on the whole border. Two major incursions, both beaten back. A total of forty-six enemy KIA, as opposed to two of our own – Paddy and the Leicester with the lung wound.

The rest of the Leicesters' company, plus a reinforced company of Gurkhas, had come down upon the Indos besieging Robinson's platoon like a horde of avenging angels, and had routed them. There had been a company of the enemy, plus a reinforced platoon farther south around the mortars. No enemy battalion. The Leicesters' OC, Wilkinson, was under a big cloud, the bastard. But for him, we'd all have been relieved at least twenty-four hours earlier, and the Leicester shot in the lung might have lived. That's what you get for relying on faulty intelligence and ignoring the men on the ground. I hoped they'd throw the book at Wilkinson.

We'd lost about a stone and a half each, and though we'd scrubbed ourselves clean in an endless series of showers, we were still covered with bites and scratches, and the civvies we were in seemed oddly light and airy. Once Robinson's men had been relieved and the Indos given a bloody nose, the combined forces of the Leicesters and the Gurkhas had swept south. We'd captured the two enemy mortars – the base plates had been too deeply sunken in the jungle floor for them to be removed in a hurry – and then we'd gone on farther south, to the Long Pa Sia ridge itself, where we'd finally located Paddy, or what was left of him.

I took another long, throat-aching swallow of my acrid beer. The wild pigs had been at Paddy's body and it was scattered all over the place. What was left of him could have been put in a handbag, and the stench was unbelievable. A friend, a comrade, a mate, reduced to that. That had definitely been the worst part.

'Boy, am I going to get drunk,' I said to the hot, dusty air.

'I second that,' Pete said.

We drank in silence until Chalky finally raised a bottle and said quietly, 'To absent friends.'

'To absent friends,' Pete and I repeated, almost in a whisper, and the three of us clinked our bottles together and drank to Paddy.

'Heard Rumour Control?' Pete asked at last, breaking the silence that had come over us.

'Nope,' I said.

'They're raising a new B Squadron.'

I turned to him incredulously. 'Bollocks.'

'No – straight up. They're going to train it up and bring it out here after A's next tour.'

The original B Squadron had been disbanded after the battle of Jebel Akhdar in 1958, amid much bitterness. At that time the future of the entire SAS had been in doubt – after all, they had disbanded the whole outfit after the Second World War. Malaysia had helped confirm the Regiment's existence. It looked like Borneo was going to ensure its enlargement.

'Where'd you get this?' Chalky asked Pete sceptically.

'The sergeant-major. He was as pleased as a two-tailed dog.'

'Must be true then. Hope they can get the right kind of blokes.'

'They need instructors at Brecon a.s.a.p. to help train them up,' Pete went on casually. Chalky and I looked at each other.

'The major told me he'd get me my stripe,' Pete said. 'I'm going to apply for the job.'

I clapped him on the shoulder. 'Good for you, Pete. You'll do well. I can just see you jumping down their throats at Brecon.'

'I have to think of the future, see.'

'About time you started getting some stripes on that arm,' Chalky said approvingly. But the atmosphere among us had changed.

Pete finished his beer. 'Anyway, I must be off. See you lads back in the lines later.'

'Cheerio,' I told him. Chalky and I did not watch him leave.

'And then there were two,' I said.

'He's lost his bottle,' Chalky said, shaking his head.

'No. He's just a bit screwed up. He'll come out of it. Remember me after Malaya? No use to man nor beast. It happens to us all.'

We sat and sipped our beer. It no longer seemed to taste as good as it had.

'Be packing up soon,' Chalky said wistfully. 'Tour's about over.'

'Aye.' Back to Hereford, I thought. For some reason the idea had lost all its appeal, like the beer.

'Pete missed some of the gen,' Chalky said.

'Oh yes? What's the next development then. And tell me it's good news, for fuck's sake.'

'They're going to train up some of the locals
– Ibans – and make some kind of scout force
out of them. And there's talk of launching raids
across the border, hitting the cunts where it
really hurts.'

My interest quickened. 'It's about fucking
time.' Then I saw his face, half grinning, half
solemn.

'Oh no. I know what's going on in that greasy
little skull of yours.'

'They want experienced NCOs, preferably
with some knowledge of Malay,' Chalky went
on innocently.

'I hate the fucking jungle, Chalky.'

'But I know you, Jock. You hate leaving a
job half finished. And besides, what's so great
about Hereford? Most of the lads are out in
Aden, covering themselves in glory.

'Covering themselves in something all right,'
I said morosely.

'I'm staying on. I've already spoken to the
boss about it. What do you say? It might be a
giggle.'

I hung my head, thinking. I would never have
admitted it for the world, even to Chalky, but I
was afraid that Pete was not the only one who
had lost his bottle lately. Paddy's death gnawed
at me – I kept thinking that there were things I
should have done differently. I knew I was not

afraid of the jungle, and that I was even quite good in it, but I still hated it. Plus, I was no longer confident in my own ability to command. And here he was asking me to start training up the natives from scratch. I just wasn't sure I was up to it, I must admit.

'When you fall off, first thing you have to do is get back in the saddle,' Chalky said in a low voice, and I looked at him, startled, wondering if he had read my mind.

'Think it over,' he said. 'But not until you've had a few more beers.' And he waved his empty bottle at the barman.

It was easily arranged in the end. They were crying out for experienced men who could speak the local lingo. I was right up their alley. So when Pete and the rest of D got on the plane back to Blighty, Chalky and I stayed behind. A Squadron was moving into the Haunted House under a young fire-eater named Peter de la Billiere, and the whole character of the war seemed to be changing with their arrival. Chalky and I spent a few days filling in de la Billiere and his blokes and generally helping them get up to speed. They'd just come from Aden, where they'd added another little slice to Regimental legend in the battle of Shi'b Taym. They'd lost a couple of good men there, and seen the Arabs display their heads for public amusement. Now they were in the mood to go through Borneo like a dose of salts.

Chalky and I were off on our own, however. We were bundled on a plane heading west, to Sarawak, Third Division's Territory, and an area that up until now had been fairly quiet, apart from the attack on Long Jawai.

The farther west we got, the more we got the impression that this was a half-baked sort of affair. But then again, I suppose that's how the SAS started in the first place. A Wessex took us to Song on the River Rejang, and there we picked up crates of weapons and ammunition. We also met up with two A Squadron blokes who were to be working with us for the remainder of the tour. One was a Geordie, Bill Starkweather, known by everyone as Starky. He was about six foot three and lean as a broomstick, with a face even a mother would think twice about loving. Not exactly the most excitable fellow in the world, he was thoughtful and deliberate. He'd smelt powder in Aden, and I think he was still turning it over in his mind.

The other guy was the opposite. He presented us with a problem, being also a Scot nicknamed Jock, a bantam-sized little Glaswegian who'd started out in the Black Watch and whose accent even I had to make an effort to understand. We called him Gorbals in the end, Gorbals Craig. He was a product of the slums, a hard-case hooligan type with a streak of pure devilment in him who had one day been given the choice between prison or the Army. He'd taken to being in uniform like a duck to water and was now a corporal, also an Aden veteran. He just loved the whole thing – most SAS blokes do, at heart – but his relish for the job was palpable.

So with these two Laurel and Hardys we loaded up the chopper and took off again, heading south-east this time, towards the valley of the River Katibas. The river carved a gap through the jungled ridges that ran along the border in this part of the world, a gap perhaps eight miles wide, very fertile and fairly settled. Our job would be to enlist Ibans from the highlands overlooking this gap and then take them farther south to where the headwaters of the River Kapuas marked the border, and there gather what information we could about enemy dispositions and movements.

There was also an unspoken understanding that at some point we would be slipped off the leash and allowed to make incursions across the border itself, to keep the enemy off balance. That, I have to admit, was something we were all looking forward to. To be able to go after the buggers on their own ground and dish out what they had been giving us for the past months; it was enough to make someone like Gorbals drool with anticipation.

The chopper landed in a fury of dust near the eastern bank of the Katibas. It took us nearly half an hour to unload her, and when she took off again and the dust had a chance to settle, I saw that we had an audience.

Perhaps a couple of dozen Iban villagers were studying us intently. The men were fearsome-looking characters, heavily tattooed, with bone needles through their noses or lower lips and heavy bone rings dragging down their earlobes to the shoulder.

I went forward, waving and grinning like an idiot, and got talking to one of them who understood some Malay. I told him we wanted to meet the local headman and he scampered off. The rest of them remained where they were to keep an eye on us, and we looked at their blowpipes with some nervousness. The natives in this part of the world were not as easygoing as the Muruts farther east, and their old head-hunting habits, it was said, were still deeply ingrained.

The headman eventually arrived, a vision of wrinkled darkness. He looked as though you could have cobbled boots out of his hide. His name was Ejok, and a couple of the younger men had to interpret for us, as the local dialect was a distant cousin of Malay. He asked us bluntly what our game was, and I told him we wanted to recruit some of his young men to fight the Indonesians on the border.

That created a buzz. The men of the nearby villages were trickling in by ones and twos, and now we were sitting cross-legged in the dirt with a semicircle of perhaps thirty around us. Gorbals and Starky were staring as intently right back at them.

What would the young men fight with? Ejok wanted to know, looking shrewdly at the crates and ammo boxes which lay piled up behind us.

I nodded at Gorbals, and he opened a crate, bringing out a Remington pump-action twelve-gauge shotgun, then an old .303 Enfield rifle, and finally a Webley revolver that looked as though it had last been fired at El Alamein. To us, these seemed a pretty poor offering, but the Ibans were impressed when we told them that we would provide weapons for anyone who joined us, and we'd also teach them how to use them.

But old Ejok wasn't to be hurried. He made a great show of mulling over our proposal while the younger men grinned and nudged each other like the bloodthirsty devils they were. Then he invited us to a feast that night in his village where he would give us an answer. I accepted with mixed feelings, foreseeing an ordeal by *jarit* and *tapai*, and Ejok strode off.

'What now?' Gorbals asked me.

'You're in for a treat,' I told him. 'A bit of a shindig.'

'Loads of booze. Great food. It'll be a blast,' Chalky explained, his words cheerier than the look on his face.

'He's a cautious one,' I said. 'Didn't invite us to stay in the village. Looks to me like he hopes to keep his options open.'

'The youngsters will go for it,' Chalky said confidently. 'I could see their mouths watering at the sight of the weapons.'

'Aye,' I said. But something didn't feel quite right. This was supposed to be a quiet area, even though it wasn't far from the border. We should have been welcomed with open arms.

'I have a feeling the Indos have beaten us to it,' I said, but then snapped myself out of it.

'Come on, let's set up camp. I want all this kit shifted into the trees and a perimeter marked out. Claymores, trip flares, the whole heap. But don't arm the claymores just yet.'

163

'You expecting trouble?' Gorbals asked curiously, and with a certain eagerness.

'I don't know. Best to be ready for it, though. Let's get stuck in.'

15

It's always the same with the Army. You never have enough time to do everything you want. It's always a hell-for-leather rush. We shifted the gear and set up camp like men possessed, determined to have it all done before nightfall. We weren't being sneaky-beaky here, so we could clear fields of fire, dig shell scrapes – the works. By the time the sun went down we'd set ourselves up nicely on the slopes overlooking the paddy-fields of the river valley.

'Starky stays here to keep an eye on things,' I ordered. 'We bring Brownings only, and mind your Ps and Qs. And Gorbals . . .' – I wagged a finger at the little Glaswegian – 'don't throw up.'

'What?'

'You heard me. This'll be your first meal with these people, so you're about to have your eyes opened. Be polite, and keep the damn stuff down.'

Gorbals looked a little pale. He laughed nervously. 'What do they eat, each other?'

Neither Chalky nor I answered him, but just looked grave, and he went paler still. I had to turn away so he wouldn't see the smile breaking out over my face. From being gloomy at being left behind, Starky began to look distinctly relieved.

The village was bustling when we got there, a fire-lit maze of stilted longhouses and dancing shadows. Kids were bounding about all over the place, competing with the pigs for space, but most of the men were in a circle around a couple of large fires with spits slung across them and a couple of carcasses turning over the flames. I saw Gorbals staring intently at the roasting shapes, trying to make out what they were. His customary cockiness had evaporated and he was gaping around like a tourist, especially at the bare-breasted girls standing at the limit of the fire-lit area, giggling and pointing.

'Out of bounds,' I hissed at him. 'Don't give them so much as a wink, Gorbals, you got that?'

'All right, Sarge. But they're awful bonny.'

'Their boyfriends probably think so too. We're here to make friends, remember, not piss them off by flirting with their daughters. Eyes front . . .'

Ejok, resplendent in a feathered head-dress, received us with great dignity and we squatted down on reed mats to either side of him. Then we were handed wooden bowls of *tapai* which we downed with a great show of relish, smacking our lips and hoping the damn stuff wasn't about to reappear in spectacular fashion.

One of the younger men was acting as interpreter between myself and Ejok. 'We have dug up some good *jarit* for you,' he translated proudly, just as the loathsome stuff appeared in trough-like lengths of bamboo.

'Jesus Christ,' Gorbals spluttered, as the smell reached him.

'It'll put hairs on your chest,' Chalky reassured him with evil glee. 'Get some more *tapai* down your neck – it makes it a bit more bearable.'

The villagers were watching us expectantly, so we had no option but to reach into the bamboo troughs and scoop up handfuls of the reeking stuff. Imagine sticking your hand into the guts of a dead dog that's been lying by the side of the road for a week and you have some idea of the experience. I closed my eyes and chewed once, then swallowed as quickly as I could, and the dirty deed was done. A gulp of the *tapai*, which seemed sweet as nectar in comparison, and when my eyes had stopped watering and my stomach had finished its attempt at retching I was able to take notice of my surroundings again.

Gorbals and Chalky were both green, but they'd held their end up. And now, thank God, in addition to the *jarit*, leaves covered in fruit and roast pork and eggs were appearing too. Everyone was tucking in like they hadn't eaten in a week, and the villagers were too busy stuffing their gobs now to notice how much *jarit* we ate.

Ejok, the wily old coot, wanted to know where the fourth member of our team was, and where we had set up camp. I fobbed him off, and steered the conversation round to the recruitment of his men. He wasn't to be rushed, though, and for my pains I was invited to take another handful of the stinking local delicacy, which shut me up for the next few minutes.

Had he or any of the other villagers run into soldiers in the surrounding jungle? I asked innocently when I had recovered.

Ejok was silent a long time after the question had been translated for him. His gimlet eyes looked me up and down. All kinds of soldiers had been seen, he answered evasively. Some in helicopters, some on foot, some in boats. What kind was I looking for?

Small men, I told him. Dark men, black-haired – like the Dyaks in the villages to the north.

He shrugged. His hunters had perhaps seen some of these men in boats on the River Kapuas. And some in the jungle. They had visited his village and warned him to inform them if the British arrived.

And now Ejok grinned, showing strong, yellow teeth, most of which had been filed to a point.

So the Indos had got here ahead of us. And Intelligence, which had assured us the area was quiet, had got its head up its arse as usual.

The knowledge that we didn't have as much time as I had hoped made me come straight to the point. Would Ejok then allow his young men to work with us, be trained by us, and fight the Indos?

The old boy paused a long time before answering. Yes, he said finally. The young men would be glad to learn new ways of fighting, and it would be good to have many guns in the village to defend it.

I didn't quite like the sound of it, but at least we'd been given the green light. His young men would possibly have joined us on their own account anyway, but it was as well that he had given his permission. That way, his authority was intact, and that was the important thing.

Then, I told him, let those men who want to be trained and to be given weapons assemble

169

outside the village at dawn tomorrow, and we would begin.

Ejok nodded, cramming his mouth full of *jarit*. He still seemed lukewarm, as if he was bowing to the inevitable against his better judgement. I had a feeling that, had we been Indonesians making the same offer to him, he might have accepted it in the same manner. He and his people were caught between a rock and a hard place.

The feasting went on for hours, and the *tapai* was doled out in never-shrinking quantities. I could already feel the potent stuff messing with my mind, so at an appropriate moment I excused myself and the team and we left, lurching off through the trees belching and groaning. Chalky and I had to halt and hold Gorbals upright while he vomited copiously into the bushes. When the smell hit me I had to bend over and do the same, as Chalky surveyed us with smug satisfaction.

'You Jocks really know how to puke, don't you?' he said. He'd drunk as lightly as a bird at the feast and felt fine.

'Fuck off,' I groaned between heaves.

'Cunt,' Gorbals whispered.

'I wouldn't worry,' he went on, undeterred. 'There's still a couple of hours before dawn.'

The sun came up on a sorry sight. We were there in body, but our spirits were straggling somewhere. I looked into Gorbals's pasty, red-eyed face and knew that it mirrored my own.

'I'll never drink again,' he said to me in a low voice.

We took up positions just to the west of the camp and watched as our new recruits came sidling up out of the valley in ones and twos. Out of the morning mist they materialized like ghosts and sat down around us with their heads in their hands. A more hung-over, malodorous, crapulent crew would be hard to imagine. It was not an auspicious start. Some were still so drunk they fell over as they tried to sit down opposite us, and began giggling madly. Others obviously had heads even more tender than Gorbals's and mine, and squatted there in morose silence.

But at least they had shown up. Over two dozen of them – enough to make a real start.

I made a conscious effort to snap out of the stupor I was in. Oddly enough, the gathering heat helped. Though it only reinforced the splitting agony of my headache, I was quickly sweating out the poisons from my system. I took continual sips of lukewarm water from my bottle to replace the crap that was oozing out of my pores and soaking my uniform.

'First things first.' I switched to Malay. 'Who here speaks this language? Hands up . . .'

All but one or two of the men raised their hands. I nodded, satisfied.

'Good. Now I want your names.' I got out a soggy notebook and scrawled them down as the men called them out. A couple of them had to be nudged and slapped by their comrades into complying.

'Chalky.'

'Yes, Jock?'

'Divide them into sections of eight. You and Gorbals and Starky will be section commanders. Gorbals, start lugging out the weapons crates.'

'Think it's safe giving them rifles, the condition they're in?' Gorbals asked painfully. I smiled at him. 'They're no worse than you. Get on with it. Starky, give him a hand.'

The men brightened perceptibly as they laid their horny paws on the weapons. None were loaded, of course, which was just as well, for within ten seconds they were all pointing them at one another and pulling on the triggers like it was an enormous joke. I saw Chalky roll his eyes. One fellow in particular was getting all the other men to put the muzzles of their weapons to his chest and in general behaving like a right prick. I grabbed him. 'What the hell do you think you're doing? Don't you know that if these things were loaded you'd be dead by now?' I batted the various rifles that were pointed at him away with a show of anger. 'These are *dangerous*. They will *kill* you. Understand?' I shouted, both at him and all the others.

He just grinned at me. 'They cannot kill me, cannot hurt me,' he said in Malay. 'I'm safe.'

'What do you mean?'

He proudly waggled a scrap of bone and feather which hung from a thong about his neck. 'This is charm, protection. This keeps the white man's guns from hurting me. I bought it over the mountain from a shaman.'

I touched the disgusting little greasy scrap. 'This'll stop you from getting shot, right?'

'Yes.'

'OK then, chum. Let's have it for a second.'

He handed it over, unease erasing the smugness from his face.

'Gather round,' I shouted so they could all hear. 'Gather round and see what the shamans can do to protect you from the white man's guns!' I felt like a character out of *King Solomon's Mines*.

I threw the charm on the ground while the Ibans crowded round, eager to see the show. Then I drew my Browning and clicked back the hammer, sighting on the charm.

'What's your name?' I asked the charmless Iban, who now looked distinctly worried.

'Batu.'

'Well, Batu, here's what your charm is worth.'
And I put four rounds into it which fairly blew
it to pieces.

There was a lot of oohing and aahing, and
old Batu looked as though someone had just
thrown his teddy bear away. I patted him on
the shoulder and said, 'White man's magic is
very strong. Don't worry – we'll teach it to you,
and you will be able to use it yourself.'

He smiled uncertainly at that.

I decided that it might be safer leaving
weapons training until the men were all a
little less hung-over. Instead I told them to go
back to their village and fetch their parangs –
we were going to do a little construction work.
They were a sullen crowd, dropping their new
weapons with obvious reluctance, but they did
as they were told, which was something. The
fate of poor old Batu's charm had obviously
impressed them.

We spent the day laying out the rough outline
of a camp, one in which we would be able to
train thirty men, and house them too, if need be.
It surrounded our first tiny bivouac and was a far
more elaborate affair. The perimeter was guarded
by eight four-man trenches. We had bugger-all in
the way of wire, but about a million sandbags, it
seemed, so they were pretty solid affairs, with
overhead protection three sandbags thick.

In the middle of this perimeter were two structures which it took us all of five days to set up. The first was a longhouse built on stilts in the local style, with a stone hearth in the middle of the floor, bamboo walls – all the local mod cons. The second was a heavily sandbagged blockhouse or bunker, two-thirds underground, the roof heavily protected with earth and sand-bags, and slits in the low walls which commanded the entire perimeter. A deeper recess within the blockhouse itself housed all our spare ammo, while Starky, who turned out to be quite good with his hands, rigged up a wooden weapon rack, and we had ourselves an armoury.

We were to be resupplied with radio batteries, rat-packs and what-not once a week by a helicopter out of Song, so we also hacked out a crude landing pad on the slopes leading up from the river. We had to cajole our new recruits into a spot of earth-moving in order to provide a level area for choppers to set down. And they weren't too pleased at having to clear several acres of brush and jungle from around the camp in order to improve our fields of fire. At the end of the first week, as requested, the chopper dropped off a few dozen coils of wire, and so we were able to surround our little home from home with a fence of sorts, though it was only a couple of coils high.

Looking back on the whole thing now, I realize it was a mistake. We were doing exactly what the Yanks would later do in Vietnam – providing a focal point for the enemy to attack. That was not our job – we were supposed to go out looking for them, not wait for them to come to us. But at the time, I just wanted the base to be as secure as possible. Everything is easy with hindsight, I suppose, but I should have seen it coming.

16

Some of the weapons we had been given to issue to the villagers were more dangerous to their new owners than to the enemy. A couple of the old .303s had to be completely written off, and getting hold of ammo for the rest involved a nightmare of form-filling. But, as the days went on, we saw to it that every man had a serviceable weapon and knew never to point it at anyone unless he wanted to kill them. Of course, before we could actually let the men fire the things there was more construction to be done – we had to rig up a shooting range just beyond the camp perimeter. There was no problem with getting the men to pull the trigger, as they loved the flash and bang side of things. But they hated to keep the butt of their weapons in their shoulders, because the rifles kicked when they went off – especially the old .303s. They had a kick like a mule. All in all, we were a sweaty and bad-tempered set of blokes by the end of our second week, but our recruits were beginning to see the light. I think Chalky privately thought I was overdoing the by-the-book training a bit. We were not supposed to fight a battle with these lads, but to teach them to be the ears and eyes of the Army. Sneaky-beaky stuff, which they were already superlatively equipped to undertake. We'd be glad we had done it later, though. Which meant that so far I had made one good decision and one bad one. Par for the course, I suppose.

Gorbals and I took out the first long patrol. I had figured out a system of dual patrolling which would provide security for the immediate area and also give the men some practice, while extending our intelligence-gathering a little. In simple terms it meant that there was always one four-man patrol doing the rounds of the region surrounding the base and Ejok's village, but never venturing farther than half a mile away from either. At the same time there was one longer-ranging patrol every day which probed south along the river to the border. The latter always had two of us troopers leading it, the former only one. And there was always one of us in base monitoring the radio, getting some kip and generally looking after the place. It was a fairly gruelling schedule, giving each member of the team only one day off in three, not counting guard duty and radio stag at night. We rubbed along on whatever sleep we could snatch, and in time grew used to it. In the meantime the Ibans became accustomed to patrol procedures and weapons handling, and obviously thought it was all a great lark, especially when they could parade through Ejok's village with their rifles, looking serious and important and winking at the local wenches.

Our first long patrol consisted, besides Gorbals and myself, of four of the most promising recruits, including Batu. We contoured south along the ridges that ran down to the Katibas until the land began to rise in jungled mountains ahead of us, where the river had its source. There was good hunting up there, Batu told me – plenty of mouse deer and wild pig – but no one lived there. Looking up at the steep-sided ridges that tumbled away to the edge of sight, I could believe him. It was a forbidding country, like something out of Conan Doyle's *The Lost World*. Small bodies of infantry might make their way through it, but it would be impassable for vehicles, and even manhandling heavy weapons such as mortars and recoilless rifles would be extremely difficult. That was good news as far as I was concerned. I for one had been mortared enough lately to last a lifetime.

We toiled up into the high country, through

virgin rain forest where it was perpetually twilight. There was no *belukar* here – the place had never been cultivated and in fact was almost wholly untouched by the hand of man. It was almost impossible to say where the border actually ran, as the maps of the area were inadequate. This was in the days before satellites and Global Positioning Systems. All we had to go on were our own bearings and pacings, and the local knowledge of the Ibans themselves, for whom this was part of their backyard.

The only feature we could truly rely on was the river itself, and, like all primitive peoples since the dawn of time, we began to look on it as a possible highway, an open road which led right into the heart of Sarawak. It narrowed as we trudged higher into the hills, becoming little more than a wide stream which a man might wade without wetting his armpits, but it was still navigable by small boats all the way to the border and beyond. I began to be convinced that it was the passage of the Katibas which was the most important factor in our area of operations. We had to dominate and control it if we were to secure the region in the north and the base itself.

To that end, our subsequent long patrols scouted out all possible sites on the riverbanks which might be used to monitor river traffic. It wasn't easy, for in places the Katibas ran through narrow gorges which acted like bottlenecks on the flow of the water and sped it up into a series of rapids. We took to taking rope with us on long patrols as a matter of course, to help us cross and recross the river when the current became too fast for a laden man to ford it safely.

Two weeks went by.

We found no trace of enemy presence anywhere along the border or the river, though A Squadron were having a few dust-ups away to the east, in our old stamping grounds. So far we had not ventured across the border itself, or where we thought it might be, and the men were getting a little restless, as the gruelling routine of patrols was wearing them down, with nothing to show for it. Then finally Starky came out of the blockhouse one morning as I was inspecting a team which Gorbals was about to lead off on a local patrol. He was grinning from ear to rear.

'Good news, Sarge. Word from on high.'

'What?' I asked irritably. I was filthy and exhausted, as were we all.

'The password came over the air – "Claret".'

That made me perk up at once. 'When?'

'Just this minute. As of now they've slipped us off the leash.'

That single word, 'Claret', meant that we were

now authorized to lead patrols across the border itself. It had been long enough coming.

'How far?'

Starky looked a little less ecstatic. 'Three thousand yards.'

'Fuck,' I said. Less than two miles. Still, it was something, and it would be good for morale to feel that we were taking the war to the enemy.

'All patrols are cancelled until further notice,' I said. 'Gorbals, stand your blokes down. We need some planning on this one. O-Group at 1800 hours this evening in the blockhouse. I want all the men ready for a kit inspection in the morning, and I'll pick who will go on the first op. Clear?'

'Oh aye!' the little Glaswegian chortled.

In the end I decided that myself, Chalky and Starky would be going, with Starky as radio operator, plus five of the Ibans. We took the PRC 351 and three days' rations. Our aim was to parallel the Katibas right over the border, and then set up an OP and monitor any river traffic for a few days. We'd be on half rations, of course, but I didn't want the lads weighed down with a lot of rat-packs. As long as we had plenty of water and ammo, I felt we'd be all right.

We set off an hour before dawn two days later, wading through a waist-high mist in the early-morning darkness, our rifles across our chests in what they would later call the Belfast Cradle. Batu was out on point. He had proven to be a wizard at woodcraft, and keen as mustard after he had got over the shock of seeing his bulletproof charm blown to bits. I was quite proud of our new recruits. They were silent as snakes as we tabbed along in single file, following the river's eastern bank, the grim-looking mountains of the border country looming up ahead of us in the growing light.

We were as attuned to the jungle as we would ever be. It was no longer an alien place to us. If you had left me there with just the little survival kit I carried in my kidney pouch, I reckon I could have lived comfortably enough till I was of an age to retire. I still didn't like it, though. I'd rather have the desert, or the Arctic or even Piccadilly bloody Circus. The only thing that kept me there was a need to see the job done, to see it through – whatever that meant. And I hadn't forgotten Paddy. I suppose you could call it unfinished business.

We made four miserable miles that first day, the ground so steep that our noses were virtually touching it as we ascended. It was knackering going, the worst ground I'd seen yet in Borneo, but we knew this part of it pretty well now, from our daily patrols. Beside us, the Katibas grew narrower and faster as the land rose, and on either side of it cliffs loomed up, shutting out the sunlight and dripping with water and gunk from the riot of vegetation that matted them all the way up to their tops. We bivvied just on our side of the border that first night, taking turns to grab an hour or two of sodden, twitching sleep. Sardines and biscuits for breakfast, and then we were on the move again before it had even become light. Within an hour we had entered Kalimantan, and were now across the border.

We had not gone more than a mile when the cliffs on either side of the river began to draw back, and the land became a hilly, ridged plateau which looked down on the green horizons of Sarawak to the north, the river rushing down out of an even higher set of hills to the south. We caught only a glimpse of the startling view, and then the *ulu* swallowed us up again.

Although there wasn't much vegetation on the jungle floor, beneath the canopy, along the riverbanks a little sunlight could get through, and there was more cover. We laid a snap ambush in case anyone was trailing us, and then settled into two groups of four. Myself, Starky and two of the Ibans set up the OP proper, just overlooking the river, in the roots of a huge tree that had fallen some time in the distant past and was now a hollow shell. The others, under Chalky, were our security. They set up fifteen yards to our rear, so that we wouldn't receive any unpleasant surprises while our attention was elsewhere. It took us the rest of the day to settle in and disguise everything, and the Ibans, thank God, cottoned on at once to what was wanted. They had lain in wait for animals like this many a time while hunting. Now they were waiting for humans.

My orders gave me a lot of leeway. Some might say enough rope to hang myself. I was to observe enemy activity on the southern side of the border, and at my own discretion I was to interfere with it if practicable. I was not intending to start up any fireworks on this patrol, but the knowledge that I *could* was comforting.

The river was a regular highway for every bugger in the jungle. Before we'd been ensconced a couple of hours the first in a long procession of vessels came cruising down the brown, oily current. A couple of the locals in a dugout canoe, trolling along as if they hadn't a care in the world, with a big dead wild pig in the bottom of the boat. Batu, who was beside me, grinned insanely, and told me one of the men was his uncle.

It seemed that more than a couple of the men from Ejok's village crossed the border to hunt, for Batu, who by now was beside himself with glee, recognized at least three more villagers as the little dugouts came drifting down past us like leaves. I was beginning to wonder if we would end up seeing anyone on the Katibas except Batu's sodding neighbours.

We lay there for three days, and saw nothing that might remotely be construed as military traffic. The men were beginning to get a little restless, and even Chalky turned grumpy on me. 'Quiet as a fucking grave down here, Jock. Those Intelligence boys couldn't find their own arse with both hands and a torch. Reckon this is a bit of a goose chase.'

But we toughed it out. Boredom is the worst enemy of any soldier while he's in an OP. It's like watching paint dry and having to find it immensely interesting for hours at a stretch.

On the fourth day I was seriously thinking of jacking it in. I had originally intended sticking it out for a week, but our new recruits were becoming increasingly switched off, and I was afraid that a couple of them might just pack it in and stomp off home. It was then that we all heard it – a mist-shrouded morning with the jungle crooning away madly to itself as usual, but some different note in the background, growing steadily louder.

Put-put-put . . . An engine, coming downriver.

I had to pull Batu forcibly down – the silly bugger had actually tried to stand up for a better view. I held my finger to my lips an inch from his face, and he nodded, grinning his demented grin.

A long, narrow-beamed boat came into view on the brown water, its outboard sputtering away, and in it were at least twelve Indonesian soldiers with their AKs pointed over the sides, their eyes studying the wall of jungle that they were cruising past.

I froze. Very faintly beside me, I could hear Starky humming *Jingle Bells*.

The boat slid away downriver, and I breathed again.

'Sarge,' Starky whispered to me. 'You know where they're heading, don't you?'

I nodded. 'Everyone pack up – fast.'

17

The pace I set was breakneck and ball-breaking. We travelled at a brisk jog when we could, throwing caution to the wind, but pausing every so often to listen and watch, just in case. No sign of anything.

I cursed the murderous terrain, the suffocating heat, the mosquitoes, the mud, and most of all, those bastards in that boat. They were heading towards Ejok's village – the first settlement on the river north of the border. And Gorbals was going to have them in his lap by early afternoon at the latest. We'd never get there in time, but we had to try all the same.

It had taken us the best part of two days to make our way to the site of the OP. Now we travelled that distance back again, or most of it, in the space of ten agonizing hours. We certainly paid for it. Starky was white-faced and staggering under the weight of the radio, and even the indomitable Batu was silent and gasping. The rest of the Ibans were not much better off. I had just decided to give them a breather when I heard it. Everyone's head snapped up. The distant crackling of gunfire, coming from the north.

'Fuck,' I said. 'Come on, lads. Time to get a move on. Starky, try and get Gorbals on the blower again.' We'd been trying to get through to the firebase for hours, but the intervening ridges had played havoc with reception. Starky had endlessly repeated a warning to Gorbals, but had received no acknowledgement, and was unsure whether it had got through.

We moved out again.

Funny – at the first sound of firing we'd all forgotten our tiredness and were now running like a bunch of shagging gazelles, even Starky, with the radio wobbling on his back. We could dispense with the map now we were in the more familiar area of our earlier patrols.

Automatic fire up ahead, and the crump of claymores going off in sequence. Some fucker was being lashed to bits by thousands of ball-bearings. They must be right in the perimeter of the base. The automatic fire rattled away from what sounded like a dozen different weapons – the bark of AKs, unlike the flatter crack of SLRs, or even the old bang of the .303s that the Ibans back at the base were mostly armed with.

Bloody awful feeling, knowing there's a mate up there – quite a few mates, I suppose – and the shit is hitting the fan all around them, and here are you bloody miles away, knowing damn well you'll never get there in time. All you can do is listen, keep moving and hope to be able to pick up the pieces afterwards.

We were running like hell at this point – I'd actually ditched my bergen – and the firing tapered off. It must have been at least half an hour between us first hearing the firing and it finishing. There were a last couple of furious crackles of full automatic, which sounded as though they were either covering a withdrawal or harassing one, and then silence. I remember thinking, Christ, let's get the bastards on the way back at least. It was an effort to remember SOPs, to pause and think for a moment. The Ibans were just as keen as we were to get at the enemy's throats, but there was no point in just charging in there guns blazing. We'd had no sitrep from Gorbals, though he might not have been in a position to give one, of course. Or to ever give one again, the unwelcome thought intruded.

The fighting was over for the moment, that was certain, and one way or another the enemy would probably be bugging out, back the way they had come, in all likelihood – it was the fastest way home.

So I got the eight of us down on the eastern bank of the river in a quick ambush formation, Starky and I as the upper cut-off, Chalky with the rest in the main killing group. I reckoned we were still at least a mile from the firebase, so we had a little time, but not much. Enough time for the red flickering to stop at the corners of our eyes, for our breathing to come back under control. The adrenalin was buzzing through me like some kind of drug, and my mind felt clear and sharp as an icicle. We might be too late to do anything for Gorbals and the rest, but by Christ, we'd hit the bad guys hard on their way out.

Starky was on the radio, still trying to get through to Gorbals, and finally something came through, garbled and static-ridden but Glaswegian-sounding. He thumped me on the arm in glee, but just then the enemy came into view around a bend in the river, and he had to turn the set down to whisper mode and I heard nothing more.

The boat came closer, with the same *putt-putting* we had heard when it had passed us on the way up. But the vessel was less full now. In fact I could see that there seemed to be only some seven or eight able-bodied men aboard, and there were two bodies lying in the bottom, with blood everywhere. Things began to look distinctly hopeful – the Indos had been given a bloody nose, it seemed; though what shape our lads back at the base were in was anybody's guess.

I can't ever remember wanting to open up so badly before. There were no orders given. I let the boat pass Starky and me and then opened up on her stern, taking out the man at the tiller first with a round to the back of the head and two more to the body as he slumped forward. Starky was firing too, and then the killing group started up with a fearsome noise. The Ibans must have been working the bolt actions on those old .303s like maniacs, judging by the volume of fire they were putting out. I just hoped they were keeping the butts in their shoulders and taking aim. Firing at a real human being is a totally different game from being on a range. Some blokes it just sends all to pieces, and they fire wild. Others it turns into bloody sharpshooters. In war, ninety per cent of all casualties, on average, are caused by ten per cent of the men engaged. I wanted results from my lot, not sound effects.

The water around the boat was stitched up into a fury of broken foam. Splinters flew from her sides. I took down another man towards the stern, as did Starky, as far as I could tell. There was almost no answering fire – the poor bastards were obviously still a little fazed by the fire-fight they had just taken part in up at the base. This fresh fight was just too much for them. Within about four seconds there was not a man upright in the boat. The tiller man I had hit had fallen over the outboard, pushing the rudder hard aport, and the boat came round in a great circle, nuzzled against the bank just upstream of us, then ran aground.

A couple of the enemy were still moving feebly, but half a dozen .303s cracked out and they jumped, then went still. That pissed me off – not so much at the time, but later, when I'd calmed down. The Ibans took no prisoners, only heads. They had to be taught differently. I knew that the Indos had killed a couple of SAS wounded who had fallen into their hands farther east, but we weren't about to descend to that level. Besides, I had to think of the intel they could have provided.

The boat was riddled, half awash and listing badly. I had thought of taking it downstream, but it was finished. So when all was quiet, Starky and the others covered Chalky and me as we investigated it. We went through the bodies for anything we could find, but there wasn't much there – no maps or documents that we could see, even in the lining of uniforms or in boots. This seemed to have been a pretty low-level raid, a reconnaissance in force perhaps.

Then we turned the Ibans loose. They went wild, stripping the dead of just about everything detachable. Rifles, ammo, boots, watches – you name it. When they produced their parangs and began slicing and hacking at the corpses, I turned away. I might have said something, but thought better of it. They had their ways, and they could keep them as long as they obeyed orders in all other respects. Besides, it would scare the shit out of the opposition to find their recce team lying headless and naked in their bashed-up boat, if they ever came this way again.

Starky shouted at me – everyone's ears were still ringing and we were talking a little louder than usual when we talked at all.

'It's OK, Sarge, it's OK. Gorbals and the others are all right. We've three wounded, but they fought them off. Claymores did the trick, it seems.'

'Thank Christ.' I felt suddenly, massively drained as the tension bled out of me. Starky was smiling, but his face was grey.

Chalky grinned wryly at me, looking old and pinched. 'Good fucking day's work, eh? These cross-border raids are really something. Especially when they do it to us.'

We cut down on the pace a little for the final approach to the firebase, not quite sure what we were about to find. In any case, everyone was laden down with the weapons and kit we had looted from the dead Indos, and the Ibans were proud as punch of their new weapons, some of them still smeared with the blood of their former owners.

We could see smoke rising, some of it from the direction of Ejok's village, which calmed the lads down considerably, but we kept together pretty well until we were down out of the rain forest and out on the flatter, more open country around the base. The jungle and brush were burning there in more than one place. Grenades had been tossed all over the place along the riverbank, in a couple of the villagers' longhouses and around the base itself. There were still a couple of bodies lying on scorched patches of brush, and the smell of cordite and burnt meat was sickening.

I could see some of our own Ibans walking around, scavenging the battlefield like ghouls. Gorbals had a burial party at work, though, and as we emerged from the trees, utterly spent, he came bobbing towards us with a smoke-blackened face and a wan smile. I went up to him and for some reason shook his hand like I was Stanley greeting Livingstone or something. It was just so good to see him in one piece. He had a wild Celtic gleam in his eye.

'What's the damage?' he asked.

'Three of our blokes got hit – one in the lung.

Doesn't look too hot – he should be choppered out a.s.a.p. The base is a wee bit smashed up, as is the village, but no great harm done. It's not like they had artillery or something. Claymores took out most of them. Silly cunts walked right into the trip-wires and then got into a right flap and began lobbing fucking white phos everywhere, trying to cover their retreat. They legged it for the river – I slotted a couple on the way. I don't suppose you ran into them on your way back up?'

'You suppose right,' I told him sombrely. 'We got them all.'

He blinked at that. 'I'll be damned. Well, one up to the good guys, eh?'

'Looks that way. How are comms up here?'

'Nothing but shite ever since you left, Sarge. Bloody typical. There's storms downriver over Song – you can see the thunderheads. We tried the Long-Range as well as the VHF, but not a sausage.'

'Keep trying,' I told him tersely. Then, in a lower voice, I asked, 'How did your lot do?'

'Not bad, all things considered. They put down a hell of a rate of fire, but whether or not they were aiming at anything in particular, I'm not sure. To be honest, the claymores got most of them, and then there were the two I potted. The enemy buggered off pretty quick, didn't press an assault. They did all right, I suppose.' Then Gorbals lowered his voice in turn. 'To be frank, Sarge, I don't know if we're running the kind of organization here that should be pitching in to a stand-up fight.'

I took this last comment on the chin. Gorbals was quite right, of course. I didn't like the way things were working out down here either. We weren't supposed to be fighting ding-dong battles with the enemy – sneaking around was more our line. And I wasn't sure the Ibans were up to the kind of experiences they'd just had. They were not soldiers, nor intended to be, but rather a kind of paramilitary scouting operation.

'You know, Sarge,' Gorbals interrupted my thoughts, 'I reckon they'll be back. That was a recce of a sort. They didn't intend to get into a dust-up with anything heavy. They thought we had some piss-arsed little police station or something here, like at Tebedu, and they could roll over us. If you got all of them, then their mates won't have learned the lesson – they'll be swanning down here wondering what happened to the first lot. And they'll be more on their guard this time.'

'That thought had occurred to me,' I said.

'What are we to do then?'

Chalky joined us. 'Good day's work, mate,' he said to Gorbals.

'Aye, right,' the Glaswegian replied distractedly. Like me, he was already thinking about the consequences. There's always something more, some other thing which comes out of a scrap. That's why the aftermath of a fire-fight is so depressing, I suppose. One of the reasons anyway.

'We need a medevac, one way or another – first priority,' I said. 'Then I'll have to have a look around at the damage. Looks to me like we got off lightly. We'll be needing more sandbags, though, and corrugated iron. I want better sangars made.'

'What's this – you going to make a fortress out of this shithole?' Chalky asked lightly.

'If we're going to stay here, then we're going to get hit here,' I stated. 'That's obvious. We'll need more people, and some heavy weapons. Maybe a couple of mortars ... Definitely an SF gimpy.'

'Far as I can see,' Chalky warned me, 'we're stretching pretty thin as it is. If you want weapons like that you'll need the blokes who can use them – regulars like us. The Leicesters and Gurkhas are off in the east, along with the rest of the squadron. You might be singing for the moon, Jock.'

'All right, all right,' I growled, growing tetchy at this blast of common sense. 'Then we may have to improvise. I'm not pulling out now –

Ejok's people will be cut to shreds if we do. There's no harm in asking Song for what we can get.'

I rubbed my eyes. 'Let the guys get their heads down for a couple of hours. Chalky, you'd better take a look at our wounded. I'll get Starky to look at the VHF. We *must* have comms re-established, or else we're just sitting here like a boil on a bum, and about as much use. The burial parties can rest when they've done their bit, and the rest of the clearing up can wait until we've grabbed some gonk.'

'Cheer up, Sarge,' Gorbals told me. 'Think of all the nice new rifles you got for the Ibans – lovely AKs. We can even use their ammo.'

'True,' I admitted. I rubbed my eyes again. 'Christ, I'm knackered.'

'Been a busy day,' Gorbals commiserated.

'The first of many,' I told him wearily.

18

It wasn't until the following morning that we were able to re-establish comms. The storm over Song had died out by then, and it was clear skies all around, or as clear as they ever get in the rain forest. The problem was that we were pretty much on our own, with no designated back-up. Anything we wanted we'd had to scrounge through official and not-so-official channels. It wasn't as if we had a squadron quartermaster behind us. A Squadron was way off in the east, along with most of the regular battalions, so trying to get hold of the equipment and the extra people I wanted was next to impossible. The whole frontier was being defended by a thread-thin line and there simply wasn't enough kit or bodies to go round.

There were pats on the back for us, of course, for having wiped out the enemy recce party. But apart from that, there was little substantial support. Make do with what you've got, was the philosophy. The bloody British Army has fought every war in its history on the cheap.

The medevac choppers came first, and suspended in slings below them were loads of corrugated iron, sandbags and wire. The three Ibans who had been wounded seemed in good spirits. I think they considered a ride in a helicopter almost worth getting shot for, judging by the looks on their faces.

And then, of course, the hard work began.

The firebase needed reworking if it was to stand off a serious assault – that much was clear now. We still had the eight four-man trenches along the perimeter, but these were now improved, with shelter bays dug in alongside them, and heavier overhead protection. We demolished the longhouse in which the men had been living, and instead constructed another dugout next to the HQ bunker. The perimeter wire was now two coils deep and three high, and we cleared all vegetation for another fifty yards out from the wire to create a two-hundred-yard killing zone. All well and good, but if we didn't have the weapons to defend it we might as well have been building sandcastles.

We had AKs for almost half the men now, and they used the same 7.62mm round as the SLRs. So instead of the hotchpotch of ammo we'd had to requisition before, it was all pretty much of a muchness, which made the paperwork easier.

What we were really short of were claymores and the like, the little items which had saved the base last time around. There were none to be had, so we decided to improvise. We used the powder from all the .303 ammo that was surplus, put it into thin cans, filled the cans to the brim with nails, stones, you name it, and augmented it with a few fragments of C4. The cans were then half-buried so that the charges would be directed upwards, and connected with det cord to flash initiators, all of which ended in the trenches. The occupants would just have to push a button to have the cans explode in long strings a hundred yards to their front. It was a clumsy, crude, awkward but hopefully effective system. Nowhere near as murderous as real claymores, but better than nothing. What we really needed were trip flares farther out, but there were none to be had. The best we got were some little packs of miniflares and a few Shermuly rocket flares.

The work around the base took us some six days. Heavy going in the heat and humidity, and the weight was dropping off all of us constantly, so that even Chalky's normally moon-shaped face was drawn and hollow-cheeked now. By the time we were done, though, I was pretty sure we could see off anything except a really determined assault, and maybe even that. The trouble was that we couldn't count on being reinforced if the shit really hit the fan. Song was only a glorified police station and supply depot manned by some loggies and Pioneers, so anything substantial would have to be choppered in from Kuching. We were on our own – same old story.

I started the routine of local patrolling again. If nothing else, it kept us familiar with the surrounding terrain, and also kept up our profile in the eyes of the locals. Nothing untoward was spotted anywhere for three miles beyond the firebase perimeter. Another week went by, a fortnight now from the last contact, and everyone was as twitchy as a cat in a thunderstorm. The brass in Kuching offered Chalky and me three days' leave in Kuching – that's how quiet it was – but we turned it down.

Then we came across something. I had taken a patrol out several miles to the south, towards the headwaters of the Kapuas. We had been out for the better part of a day, and night was not far off when Batu – who had become a first-rate soldier by any standards and was invariably our point man – halted and went into a crouch just in front of me.

Starky was behind me with the radio, and then two more Ibans. We all froze, our rifles pointing out into the gloom of the surrounding jungle.

Batu signalled me forward. When I joined him he pointed wordlessly at the ground.

It was hard to see in the swiftly dimming light, but there in the mud of the forest floor were the unmistakable tracks of booted feet. And, at the side of the trail they had made, the white stub of a cigarette end.

'Shit,' I murmured.

Batu cast about like a hound on a scent and came up with three more trails. On these, the tracks overlapped one another.

'How many?' I asked the little Iban quietly. His forehead furrowed. The jungle peoples aren't good at imagining any number over five.

'As many as in the boat?' I asked him.

He shook his head. 'More. Many more,' he said in Malay. 'And see' – here he drew my attention to the depth of the tracks – 'men carrying things, heavy things.' He hunted around and then showed me what looked like the mark of a wheel in the mud. It puzzled him, but not me. It was the impression left by the base plate of a light mortar. Whoever had been carrying it had set it down for a second to rest.

We followed the tracks for perhaps a couple of hundred yards, but by then night had swooped in on us, so we halted to get our bearings.

The numerous tracks had been all heading north, but at one point the heavily laden men had diverged, a party of them heading off westwards. Obviously the mortar section was going to set up on the higher ground there, in easy range of the firebase, and also in a position to command the approaches from Song and the river itself. These lads – perhaps as many as a full company of them judging by the heavily marked trails – were after our scalps. There was no time to sit around. I gave everyone ten minutes to rest, and then, trusting in my compass, I began leading us back to the base in the raucous darkness, while Starky, panting behind me, gave Chalky a sitrep and prepared the others for what was to come. We had weathered one squall, but now the storm was well and truly on its way.

19

I'll never forget that hectic, blundering, exhausting trek back to the base. We were cut and clawed to ribbons by *rotan* and heavy, saw-edged leaves, and crashed flat on our faces every five yards. Every so often we'd stop dead and listen for a few minutes, for what it was worth. The jungle around us was silent as a tomb. I doubted if the enemy would try to travel at night, and Chalky assured us over the radio that there was no sign of activity to his front, but he had the entire garrison on stand-to.

The night seemed endless. By my watch we had perhaps an hour to go before dawn when we saw it – the shatteringly bright burst of a star-shell in the sky to the north. Mortar-launched illumination. It seared our night vision to nothing and left us blinking away red and purple after-images.

'Fuck!'

The radio crackled. Starky rogered a message

and then grabbed me by the shoulder, his usual imperturbability vanished.

'They're hitting the base,' he hissed.

I didn't have to be told. The quiet of the night had been blown to pieces by long rattles of automatic gunfire to the north. More star-shells went up, brightening the entire sky.

'Let's move,' I said, and set off at a run.

There was no need to worry about making noise. A massive fire-fight had developed up ahead, deafening crackles of gunfire and the bangs of exploding grenades accompanied by the all too familiar crump of mortar rounds impacting. Chest heaving, I halted the patrol and we crouched in All-Round Defence, gasping for air and trying to make some sense out of the din. We were close enough to see the arc of red tracer criss-crossing the night sky, and the mortars were sending up more illum every few minutes, creating a silver, shadowed world under the jungle canopy, everything the colour of ash. Stupid bastards. The illum would help the defenders more than the attackers. I supposed they wanted to have a look at the layout of the base, something they should have done in daylight. We were not dealing with elite troops here, obviously, but if there were enough of them, and they were sufficiently bloody-minded, it wouldn't matter.

'Get me Chalky on the blower,' I said to Starky.

A moment later he gave me the handset.

'Echo Three Zero, this is Echo Three One. Over.'

'One, this is Three Zero.' I actually had to raise my voice to make myself heard over the racket. 'We are figures three-zero-zero yards outside your lines. Send sitrep. Over.'

There was a pause of perhaps a minute. When Chalky came back I could hear the fire-fight over the handset as well as with my other ear.

'Three One, we have four wounded. Estimate enemy in company strength with mortar support and one SF MG. Ammo OK for now. No enemy casualties that I can see – they're staying in the trees and hosing us down. Over.'

'Roger, wait. Out,' I responded. The Indos were not quite the chumps I had thought. They were going to soften up the base before moving in, hence the illum. They were concealed by the trees and thus could use it with impunity. And if they had a Sustained Fire Machine-Gun – that is, a weapon mounted on a tripod – as well as mortars, then they could afford to sit back for a while and soften the place up.

I got hold of Chalky again. The firing rose and fell with little pattern to it. As Chalky had said, they were simply hosing the place down.

'Three One, have you got word through to Sunray? Over.' That was the code for the local district commander in Kuching.

'Negative. We're still trying. Over.'

Fuck. 'Roger that. Can you hold? Over.' I was talking about our Ibans. I knew that Chalky and Gorbals would hang on till the end.

'Do we have a choice? Over.'

I grinned, and made a quick decision. 'Roger your last. I am going to hit them from out here. Keep up your fire. Over.'

'Roger. Good luck, Jock. Out.'

I turned to Starky. 'Stay here. I'm going forward for a closer look.' He nodded, eyes shining with adrenalin in the darkness. I could see in them the ribboned reflections of the tracer in the sky behind me.

I took Batu with me, tapping him on the shoulder. He was trembling, but smiled, wide-eyed as an owl, sweat streaming down his face. We moved forward at a crouch, rifles in the shoulder. The firing had died down a little but my ears were still hissing with white noise. Gunfire, real gunfire, is incredibly loud, but I've never once in a fire-fight heard my own weapon go off, even though it was tucked up against my ear. The mind can play strange tricks.

We edged forward until we could see the brightly lit killing zone we had cleared around

209

the firebase. The enemy was invisible, but from the black wall of the surrounding jungle shot out red streaks of phosphorus-tipped bullets, and the whole perimeter twinkled with muzzle flashes. The enemy seemed to have taken up position in a semicircle to the north of the base, cutting it off from possible reinforcement. There seemed to be no one in our immediate area. I saw that if we moved to our left, we could flank them, if a single fire team can be said to outflank an entire company.

I sent Batu back to bring up Starky and the other Iban, Jagoi. We lay watching the show while I turned a possible plan over in my mind.

'Do you think they'll assault?' Starky asked me.

I nodded. 'We've pissed them off, that's why they've brought up an entire company. My guess is they intend to wipe us out here. It'd be a big political coup as well as everything else, and it would ruin our standing with the locals. They're out for our knackers.'

'Terrific,' Starky mumbled. 'How do we change their minds?'

I didn't answer. I was wasting useless minutes silently cursing our radios. They always worked perfectly until the moment they were badly needed. It's been the same in all wars.

When the 1st Airborne dropped into Arnhem they discovered that not one of the fifty radios that had been working perfectly the day before was functioning.

The firing picked up again. I could see where the SF machine-gun was posted on the eastern slopes of the hills leading down to the river, perhaps three-quarters of a mile away. It spat tracer like the maw of an angry dragon. I could see the red lines stabbing into the base, some of them bouncing up into the night sky as they ricocheted. With four men outside the perimeter, two medevacced after the last scrap and four more wounded, Chalky had less than two dozen men to hold the base with. It didn't look good.

'We have to take out that SF,' I said quietly, and the plan, if it could be called that, leapt into my head.

'Let's go.'

The other three followed me without question as I led them away from the spectacle.

We were already exhausted, but I set a tearing pace through the *belukar* which dominated the slopes leading down to the river. Ejok's people had cleared the primary forest from the area surrounding their village generations in the past, and then had abandoned fields and other village sites as the soil became exhausted. The vegetation here was a riotous nightmare in the dark, and if we tried to get through it, it could take all night. I consulted my compass and struck out west, towards the river and the village.

It took perhaps fifteen minutes, and in that time the firing had died down except for the occasional crack of a single round. I guessed that the Indos were shaking down into assault formations; their platoons were probably on their way to the start-line for the attack. Starky extorted another sitrep from Chalky as we forged along, and breathlessly told me that there were two more wounded, and ammo for the AKs was down to four mags per man. The Ibans had been blowing it away like it was going out of fashion, ignoring frenzied fire-control orders from Chalky and Gorbals. Casualties would have been worse but for the fact that the mortars had been concentrating on the killing zone between the treeline and the wire rather than the sangars in the base itself. Clearly they had been trying to disrupt any defensive devices we had laid there preparatory to an assault.

The river was visible through a gap in the foliage in front of me, shining in the starlight. I paused to gulp for breath, and then waded in.

'Come on!' I hissed as the others hesitated.

'It'll fuck up the radio, Sarge,' Starky protested.

'Tell Chalky we're heading upriver to jump that SF from the rear, and then dump the set. And fucking hurry it up!'

The riverbank was oozing, viscous mud which sucked us in knee-deep. We kept close to the concealing vegetation of the bank, and waded along in water up to our necks, rifles held above our heads. Water shouldn't have fucked them up, but I didn't want to take any chances.

Another fifteen minutes of this. It was slow, but we made better time than we would have slogging through the *belukar*. I kept expecting to hear the fire-fight explode back into life as the Indos assaulted the base, but all we could hear was some harassing fire from the SF. The mortar barrage had stopped.

At last I crawled out of the foul-tasting water and slopped through the mud of the bank into the trees. We were all covered with glistening muck, but the rifles were still relatively free of it, which was the important thing.

I got my bearings. The eastern slopes of the hills were ahead of us. We shouldn't have far to go, but time was running out fast. I hauled the others to their feet. Batu and Jagoi were just about done in.

We set off at a staggering trot, Starky bringing

up the rear and shoving along the two flagging Ibans.

No plan survives contact with the enemy, someone once said – Napoleon, I think. Damn right. I just about collided with the Indo sentry and his muzzle flash blinded me as he opened up. I fired wildly, four or five shots, at least one of which hit him. I couldn't see a damn thing, though. It was Batu, behind me, who raced forward and finished him off with a short burst. One of the empty cases the AK ejected hit me on the right eyelid, stinging like hell. We halted, breathing madly, glaring out into the darkness, but the bugger seemed to have been alone. The Indos had obviously posted him there to keep an eye on their flank, a case of too little too late. I squeezed my eyes open and shut, waiting for that sun-bright after-image to stop glaring across my vision.

'All right, come on,' I whispered, when I could see the night in normal shades of black and grey again.

I turned to my left, to put a dog-leg between us and any other enemy soldiers who might have been stationed on this flank. We found ourselves slogging uphill on the slopes which led away from the eastern bank of the river, now paralleling the rear of the enemy line. The SF was still letting off long bursts of fire. We were above it now, and could look down to the base itself on our right, seeing the jets of tracer probing it.

Then it began. The fire-fight suddenly blew up again, and all along one side of the treeline the glitter of muzzle flashes started. I saw a rocket flare soar into the air from the base and come sailing gently down from the top of its arc, swaying under its little parachute. It lit up the entire area, and let me see the dark figures of men dashing by sections across the killing zone. The assault had begun. The Indos were using Fire and Manoeuvre, some platoons keeping the defenders' heads down while others dashed forward.

We did some dashing ourselves then. Something caught my forehead and ripped it open in the dark, but I didn't pause. The source of the SF tracer was only a few dozen yards to our right. I halted and got the other three into line, and then Baku and I sprinted forward. We halted, rifles in the shoulder, and I shouted, 'Go!', and Starky and Jagoi ran forward in their turn. We leap-frogged like this for perhaps thirty yards – hard to tell how far in the crowded darkness – and then I saw the SF crew – two men – outlined in scarlet and yellow flame as they served their weapon. I opened up on them, double-taps on one and then the other. The rest of the fire team

215

joined me and we blew the hell out of them and the vegetation for ten yards around.

'Come on!' I had to yell in order to be heard above the racket of the battle that was now raging right in the perimeter of the firebase. We gave Jagoi and Batu arcs of fire to cover our back, and then Starky and I kicked aside the shattered bodies of the two machine-gunners and sighted down the barrel of the SF. Long strings of flashes were erupting within the killing ground as the defenders set off the buried charges which had survived the mortar barrage, but the whole area was crawling with the enemy, the base flickering with gouts of flame from rifle muzzles, miniflares being fired up one after the other like fireworks. Starky slapped a two-hundred-round belt of ammo into the breech and banged shut the top cover on the machine-gun, then I re-cocked her to be sure and opened up on the bastards, long strings of automatic fire belching from the shuddering weapon. They were right up in the trenches as far as I could see, but more of them were still darting across the open killing ground, and I had a perfect field of fire. I mowed the fuckers down, barely heard the dead man's click before Starky had slapped in another belt of ammo – it was lying all over the place like shiny brass snakes – and let loose again. I heard someone shouting hoarse obscenities and realized it was my own voice, so bit my lips shut and kept the pounding butt of the machine-gun in my shoulder.

We fired off five more belts, a thousand rounds, and were scrabbling on the ground for more when the jungle erupted in a spray of leaves and broken branches ten yards to our front.

'What the fuck . . . ?' Starky shouted.

'Mortars,' I yelled back. 'The game's up. Time to clear out.' I reckoned I had got quite a few of the attackers, but I didn't know if I had saved the base or not. It hadn't looked too encouraging down there, and we had no radio now to get a sitrep. Gorbals and Chalky might as well have been on the moon.

Another mortar round impacting close by, and then another. The buggers knew their stuff, I had to give them that.

'Bug out,' I yelled, and the others followed me as I set off westwards like a bat out of hell, away from the base. What a fuck-up, I was thinking as we crashed through the jungle blindly. What a total fuck-up.

The mortar rounds chased us like sentient things, their crews walking them away from the base – the logical thing to do. There was nothing for it but to keep running and hope that some of our comrades in the valley below had got away.

*   *   *

It was a long night. I thought it would never bloody well end. We bugged out until we were a mile or so north of the base, and then got into All-Round Defence and lay listening to the mayhem in the distance. None of us spoke. Me, I was thinking of the lads in the base, and I felt particularly worm-like at having cut and run, but when I ran it through my mind, as I did again and again through the rest of the night, I just couldn't see anything else we could have done. The whole area back there was swarming with the enemy. We'd have been taken out in short order once they pinned us down, and even if the base still stood we'd never make it across the bare-arsed killing zone to rejoin the others. I knew we had badly disrupted the enemy attack, but I couldn't forget the glimpse I'd had of those tiny shadows fighting in the very trenches. The enemy had made it inside the perimeter, that much was clear, but had they been chucked back out again, or had they overrun the place? I had to take a look. Song was over fifty miles upriver and I wasn't going to run back there with my tail between my legs without even knowing the fate of the others. Shoot and Scoot, be damned.

So we lay there wide-eyed and hyped-up all night, and when sunrise came it seemed like some kind of miracle. I looked around at my companions. We were all indescribably filthy, scratched and bleeding from dozens of unnoticed little wounds. More ominously, the ammo pouches of the two Ibans were open and gaping. When I did a quick count, it became clear that we had perhaps one full magazine left each – Batu and Jagoi had been blowing it away without thought, often on full automatic. I didn't have the heart to tear a strip off them, though. They'd done pretty well, all things considered.

'What's the plan, Sarge?' Starky asked me, his voice a hoarse rasp, his eyes red-rimmed in a blackened face. He looked like a survivor from some great natural disaster. I suppose we all did. When I frowned, flakes of brown dried blood and mud fell off my forehead, and my right eyelid was swollen almost shut from where the hot cartridge case had struck it. I'd hardly noticed at the time, but now it was stinging like hell.

'We go back,' I said quietly. 'We go back and see what's left. The Indos won't hang around – they've probably buggered off already.'

Starky nodded, satisfied, but when I repeated myself in Malay, Batu and Jagoi looked distinctly uneasy, and wouldn't meet my eyes.

Everyone at the base must be dead, Jagoi told me. There was no point in going back.

'What about your friends, your fellow villagers?' I asked him. 'Don't you want to know if they're alive or dead?'

He went sullen on me, refusing to answer. I saw that anything I said would be useless, and so we compromised. I told him and Batu to head back to Ejok's village and see what things were like there. Starky and I would return to the firebase alone.

Jagoi nodded readily, obviously relieved, but Batu still seemed troubled. He told me haltingly that he would go wherever I led him. I could have kissed him, but instead ordered him to go with Jagoi. I could see that even he, bundle of enthusiasm though he usually was, had had enough. I couldn't blame him.

We parted company with many handshakes and much mock-hearty shoulder-slapping, and then Starky and I watched the two Ibans disappear into the jungle noiselessly. I never saw them again.

20

'And then there were two,' Starky said, smiling slightly.

'More than that, I hope. Let's get a push on.'

We compromised between the need for haste and the need for stealth. I suppose you could say we headed towards the base at a hasty creep.

The jungle was unusually quiet, as if the racket of the previous night had gobsmacked all the local fauna into silence. We moved as noiselessly as we could, nerve ends raw and tingling, our eyes bulging out of our heads. I had eighteen rounds left, Starky about the same. We'd cleaned our weapons as best we could during the night, but you can't do a thorough job of it in pitch-darkness – the carbon inside the gas-plug is a particular bastard to get out – and I had a feeling the SLR might just jam on me if I let off more than one or two rounds. Not that I had many more than that to let off anyway.

My ears were still hissing with white noise, the echoes of last night's fire-fight, and despite the adrenalin that was still tootling through me, I felt limp as a boiled rag. Also, there was too much in my head. You shouldn't think too much when you're out in the field – just concentrate on the world in front of your nose. But I was having major second thoughts about almost everything in my entire life at that moment. I was genuinely terrified of what I might find once we got back to within sight of the base, and I would cheerfully have put a bullet in my own head right there and then if in return I could have guaranteed the lives of the men I'd left back there. Melodramatic bullshit, I know, but true none the less. Not the kind of thing I'd be happy to brag about back in the mess at Hereford.

We passed broken, bruised spots in the jungle where the mortars had come down, and chanced across two distinct blood trails heading south-west, the blood old and solid. There were tracks, too, enough to make us feel more than a little nervous. We boxed around them and approached the base from the north-east. It took us half the bloody morning, but we had no idea what we might run into, and we'd done enough blind charging around the night before.

At last, we were at the treeline, looking out across the killing zone towards the base itself.

The sight made us drop to a crouch. I heard Starky behind me mutter 'Christ' in quiet wonder.

Bodies everywhere, littering the killing zone like fallen fruit. Perhaps three dozen of them, already blackened and swelling in the morning heat. Some were hung stiffly on the perimeter wire, others lay in tangles just in front of the sangars. Many were in pieces.

The killing zone was a muddy, shell-pocked no man's land that stank of cordite and rotting flesh. It looked like the aftermath of the Somme in miniature, a ghastly, fetid nightmare. I'd never seen anything like it before, in all my years with the Regiment.

'Looks like we gave as good as we got,' Starky said, in a strangled attempt at gallows humour.

'Aye.' I still had my binos. I had hung them around my neck what seemed like days ago now, tucking them into my shirt so they wouldn't flap around. Now I brought them out and found that they had given me livid bruises on my chest which ached in concert with the other little injuries all over me. I wiped the filthy lenses and scanned the firebase with them.

No signs of human life. There were bodies in the base itself, and some were the un-uniformed corpses of our Ibans, others the green-clad shapes of Indos. No one was moving, but scrawny carrion birds were pecking at the bodies, and I glimpsed a forest pig rooting at an Indo corpse. I scanned the inner perimeter with an awful sinking feeling, and finally stopped at a uniformed body which had a head of reddish hair.

'Sarge?' Starky asked softly.

I shook my head, lowering the binos and feeling about eighty years old.

'Can't see anything,' I lied. 'We'll head in for a closer look. I reckon the Indos have definitely buggered off. Probably expecting some kind of QRF to arrive.'

'Sarge . . .'

'Let's go.'

The wire had been cut in several places and we entered the perimeter at one of them. We dashed across the killing zone feeling as exposed as a cockroach on a tea tray, and made it into the lee of the main bunker. It was worse, much worse, up close. Here we could make out faces we remembered on the hulks of rotting meat that lay scattered around. One of our Ibans was still kneeling upright, struggling with a jammed .303 in death, the back of his head blown away.

I felt an anger so intense it dizzied me, but kept walking until I was standing over Gorbals's body. I stared at the blood in the red hair. He lay in a pool of it, his legs splintered fragments. As I watched, it oozed lazily from around the stump of an ankle.

Jesus Christ, he was still alive!

'Starky!' I bellowed.

I was searching my webbing feverishly for field dressings. Starky came running over. His jaw dropped.

'Get the fucking first-aid stuff from the bunker,' I yelled at him. He dashed off again.

Gorbals had bled almost white. He had tried to stuff a couple of dressings over the gaping holes in his legs and they had helped a little, but it didn't look good. I was swearing at him as I ripped out my own dressings and padded his ankle stump with them. He must have been caught by a mortar round.

His eyes opened, clear and blue. I was nearly as shocked as if a corpse had spoken.

'Jesus! Gorbals!'

He was croaking something, trying to speak. I read his lips and ripped out my water bottle and let the brackish, lukewarm remnant that was in it dribble over his lips.

He blinked slowly. '. . . Fucking kept you . . . ?' I heard him whisper. And then some terrible urgency came into his bloodshot eyes. He actually raised his head off the ground, his hair pulling free from the glue-like mud and blood it lay in. I supported it with one hand.

'They took Chalky.'

'What? What did you say?'

Starky threw himself down beside me, arms full of field dressings, morphine ampoules, tears streaking his filthy face.

'Chalky's alive,' Gorbals whispered. 'Indos took him . . .' The head fell back and the eyes closed. The hero dies thus in the films, but we weren't about to let that happen.

'Gorbals, you fucker!' I shouted, and began pounding his chest with my fist, then bent over and gave him mouth to mouth.

We worked on him for maybe three or four minutes, Starky and I, and then he gave a feeble gasp, and the eyelids fluttered again.

'Come on, you wee Glaswegian bastard, stay with us,' I whispered.

The eyes opened once more, and he actually smiled at us. 'Some fight, Sarge. Some fight . . .' He coughed a little, and then his gaze seemed to fix in place, staring out over my shoulder at something we couldn't see. The breath went out of him in a long, hollow sigh.

Starky and I knelt beside his body, heads bowed, for a long time.

21

It was hard – awful hard – to get my mind moving again. I closed Gorbals's eyes and looked at Starky. He seemed utterly washed out.

'What now?' he asked.

I stood up and looked around me. I already knew what I was going to do, of course, but it wouldn't be right to involve him. There was no military sense involved.

'I want you to get word to Song. Have a look around for the radio. If it's fucked – and I reckon it probably will be – then head down to the village and get a couple of Ejok's people to paddle you upriver. You should be able to make it to Song in a couple of days at most.'

Starky rubbed his eyes tiredly. 'What about you?'

'I'm staying here,' I lied. 'I've got things to do.'

He thought about it for a moment and then nodded. 'Sarge, the body . . .'

'Some of our blokes escaped, I'm pretty certain. There aren't more than eight or nine of them lying about here. I reckon they legged it into the jungle, maybe even before the final assault. Tell Ejok to gather his men together and bury the dead here. He can scavenge whatever he can.'

'Why don't you . . . ?'

'I'm going to have a scout around the area, check the enemy really has gone. The main thing is to get reinforcements down here fast.'

'What about Chalky?' Starky said.

'Never mind about Chalky. Just do as you're told.'

He blinked. 'All right then.' Then he shambled off in the direction of the battered main bunker.

I watched him go. When he had disappeared inside, I bent down and went through Gorbals's ammo pouches. He still had two full mags. I took them gently and straightened again.

The world spun for a moment. I hadn't eaten or slept properly in days, and part of me was wondering how rational I was at this moment. The proper thing to do would have been to wait for the reinforcements to arrive and then to set out after Chalky. But he could have been tortured to death by then. I was beginning to feel that all my decisions had turned out badly. I had to try and make it up. At least this way the only person I could get killed was myself.

I set off at a trot. Three almost full magazines, an empty water-bottle, and a couple of packs of biscuits. I was not exactly overequipped. I actually stumbled across a grenade on my way out of the perimeter, still grasped in the fist of a dead Indo, the pin straightened but not pulled out. I prised it out of his stiff, slimy fingers and curled back the ends of the pin so it wouldn't fall out, pocketed it, then went on.

It was not hard to find the trail of the withdrawing enemy. I cast about like a hound on a scent to the south of the base for perhaps half an hour, and struck upon a smashed broken slot heading into the rain forest, the earth churned up into a mire by heavy boots. Impossible to tell numbers, but as there were maybe forty of them lying dead about the base, I could count on another sixty at least. I'd have to watch my step. Literally. Had I been in their shoes, I'd have detailed a section to lay booby-traps behind me to slow up any pursuit. This was no time to go charging ahead.

So I followed the trail at a snail's pace, my eyes scanning every leaf and branch, a small, reed-like stick held out in front of me to check for trip-wires. I came upon one before I'd gone a hundred yards. The wire led to a grenade with the pin half out. I disarmed the thing and added the grenade to my meagre arsenal, then crept on.

The morning went by at a sweltering, humid crawl. I had to rip the sleeve from my shirt and tie it around my forehead to keep the sweat out of my eyes. I came across a stream I had known from previous patrols, and filled my water bottle, dropping in a few puritabs to kill off creepy-crawlies. Part of me knew I was off my rocker for doing this, but at that point in time I really didn't give a shit.

Farther east, the Indos had captured an SAS bloke from A Squadron. He'd been shot in the leg, and they'd tortured him by jabbing bamboo slivers into the wound. Then, when they'd had to move on, they'd simply shot him. I'd known Chalky a long time. I couldn't sit around and let it happen. It was that simple.

There was a blood trail in the torn-up mud I was following, and many of the tracks were very deep. Men carrying things – probably their wounded. Sure enough, another half-mile along the trail I came to a spot where they'd hacked down bamboo staves to make stretchers. You slide them through the sleeves of a jacket and stick the wounded bloke on top. It's crude, but better than carrying him on your back. The only problem is that it incapacitates two able-bodied men for every injured one, since they become bearers, not fighters. Good news for me.

Another booby-trap. A little more sophisticated this time – they clearly weren't in so much of a hurry now that they were clear of the base. A trip-wire again, but this time it was attached to a flash initiator, which in turn was linked by camouflaged det cord to half a dozen small charges of C4. They'd looted it from our stores, I realized. I thought of Pete the enthusiastic bomb-maker. He was probably in Brecon now, watching over men who were slogging through the Fan Dance during Selection. I felt as though I'd been in Borneo a year, though it had only been a few months.

I disarmed the charges and carefully collected up all the paraphernalia. You never know when a little C4 will come in useful.

The morning staggered on. Around me, the jungle fauna were creating their usual din again. I had come far enough from the base for them to have got over the commotion of the night before. I was glad. Silence in the jungle is eerie, like a deserted railway platform.

The trail took a right after a while, striking out almost due west. I was only a couple of miles from the border here. What were they playing at?

Another half a mile. Tiredness was beginning

to clog my thinking. I was lurching along like a clockwork toy. But my head came up when I saw the gleam of the river through the trees. The trail ended there. I found the marks of boat bottoms in the mud of the bank. The bastards had taken to the water.

I sat down, totally fucked and at something of a loss. What now?

I think I actually dozed off for a few minutes, because when I heard the noise it made me jump like a hare. The swish of a paddle in the water. I bundled myself into the undergrowth, my heart threatening to jump out of my throat.

An Iban hunter paddling downstream out of Kalimantan. Bingo.

I broke cover and waved, yelling hello in Malay.

I think I scared him almost as much as he had me. He started, stared, and then began paddling as fast as he could go. He was almost abreast of me. Not one of Ejok's people. He must have been from a tribe farther north.

I wasn't going to shoot him, but I needed his boat. I took out a grenade, popped the pin and, after waiting a couple of seconds, threw it into the water just ahead of him.

The result was spectacular. The sound of the explosion was muffled by the water, but it threw up a fountain of foam which capsized the boat and tossed the terrified Iban into the water. If I'd held on to the damn thing another second I reckon it might have gone off in mid-air. The fuse must have been faulty. But it had done the trick. The panicked boatman was striking out for the far bank as though the Loch Ness monster was at his heels. But the precious boat was drifting downstream, away from me. I threw off my webbing, dumped the SLR and dived in after it.

I thought I was going to founder before I'd reached it, but managed to grab the stern and tug it back towards the eastern bank after me. The paddle was gone, but I'd soon make a new one. And if I'd wanted a fish supper I could have had my pick. Scores of dead fish were floating on the surface of the river.

I staggered ashore, dragging the dugout after me. It seemed heavy as a corpse. Then I collapsed in the mud, gasping. The boatman had disappeared, no doubt to spread among his tribe tales of wild river marauders.

I had to take a moment to eat a few biscuits and sip some water. Then I whipped out my knife and fashioned myself a new paddle from a nearby branch. It wouldn't be as efficient as the one I had missed, but it would do. Twenty minutes after first sighting the boatman I was on my way again, this time paddling upriver, kneeling in a cockleshell of a canoe and trying to keep the bow pointed forwards and my eyes on the river ahead.

I paddled along exhaustedly for another three to four hours. The sky darkened as the afternoon came on, and I was battered by a vicious downpour. I had to pause to bale out my little vessel with my bare hands, and got the fright of my life when a huge water snake popped its head up over the prow to have a look at me, before buggering off again.

The rain passed with a few mutterings of thunder, and the jungle around me steamed as the sun came out again. I was well over the border now, beyond even the limits of penetration allowed by Claret. I became warier, expecting to run into an enemy patrol boat around every bend. I kept close to the eastern riverbank, so it would be easy to stay concealed under the overhanging limbs of the trees there, but it meant I had to bend almost double as I paddled, and a sharp, cramp-like pain began to shoot up and down my spine.

Luckily, I heard them long before I saw them. The familiar sound of an outboard came drifting round the bend ahead, and I was able to propel the canoe right into the concealment of the trees on the eastern bank with a mighty heave of my paddle, just before an Indo patrol boat hove into view. It was manned exactly as the one we had shot up weeks before, but the men in it were obviously much more alert, scanning both sides of the river intently with their rifles at the ready.

The sound of my heart rose up out of my throat in great rushing thumps as they passed, and cramp shot agony through my thighs, but I remained dead still until they had passed.

The river was no longer safe, that was clear. I climbed out of the canoe and stashed it, before continuing on foot. I kept the water in view on my right and followed it south.

The afternoon was drawing on. I wondered just how far away the Indos had their base. Not too far, I hoped. The corpses around the firebase had had no rations of any kind in their webbing, so I had assumed that their starting point must be less than a day's travel south, but I was beginning to wonder.

It was the sound of voices that halted me, and then the noise of a vehicle's engine up ahead. I nosed forward through the trees and saw a brightness ahead, which meant a clearing of some sort. I crept up to within maybe ten yards of it, and found myself looking right into the enemy base. Hey presto, there it was. I couldn't believe it had been so easy.

It wasn't much to look at. A series of

longhouses built much like those of Ejok's village except that there was more corrugated iron used in their construction, and they were set in orderly rows. There was also an MT yard with three ancient-looking trucks, and a jetty which reached out into the river and had a couple of patrol boats tied up at it. I noticed big oildrums on both the jetty and in the MT yard, obviously fuel, and there was one finer-looking building, made entirely of the ubiquitous corrugated iron, which had a couple of aerials sticking out of it, possibly a headquarters or radio shack. Looming over it all was a crude watch-tower with a bored-looking sentry leaning on its rail. There was a rough perimeter marked by a single coil of wire, but no killing zone cleared around the base, and no sangars or trenches. Hardly a sandbag in sight. Obviously the Indos did not expect to be attacked here.

There were a few soldiers strolling around, a couple working on the trucks and one at a gap in the perimeter wire which could vaguely be called a gate, but no sign of the sixty or so men I had pursued here. On the other hand, the MT yard was big enough for a dozen vehicles, only three of which were in evidence, so they might have been moved on. The place hardly looked big enough to accommodate a full company anyway.

Was Chalky still here, or had he been moved on

too? My heart sank as I considered the possibility. I had probably come on a fool's errand, but now that I was here, I was going to see it through to the bitter end, if bitter it had to be. I would have given my left ball for the chance to call in an air-strike, though.

No chance of doing anything useful while it was daylight. I looked at the sky through the overhead canopy. Perhaps two hours until dark. I decided to wait for nightfall before making my move.

22

While daylight remained I watched the comings and goings in the base and catalogued them all in my head. As far as I could make out, there could not have been more than two dozen men in the place. The rest had definitely been brought here as a jumping-off point for the attack on our own firebase, and on their return had been dispersed again. This was a mere patrol base, no more. There was probably a town with a proper garrison and barracks some distance away, connected by road – hence the trucks.

I had made up my mind that Chalky, if he were here, must be in the headquarters hut, as I had labelled it in my head. I'd try there first. Even if he wasn't there, I'd probably be able to pick up some good intelligence, and have something to cover my arse with when – and if – I got back across the border. As I lay there, I unloaded my three magazines and picked out the red-tipped tracer bullets from them. I had six in all. These

I taped to the stock of the SLR. Then I did a little work with my small store of C4 and other goodies.

Night came down with its customary abruptness. They had kerosene lamps in the base, and I watched them lit one by one in the longhouses and out on the jetty. I could see only two sentries, one in the tower and one on the gate. Unless they had night vision devices, which I very much doubted, there was no way they could monitor every inch of the perimeter wire. Most of it was outside the light cast by the longhouses. So long as I didn't make a racket, I reckoned I could make it through the wire without too much trouble.

I crawled up to the perimeter on my stomach. Laughter and talk were coming out of the longhouses; it sounded as though they were sitting down to their evening meal. The guy on the gate was smoking a cigarette, its end glowing like a firefly in the darkness.

Sweat dripped off my nose, and my palms were slippery with it. My eyes stung, and I ached from a dozen little scratches, gashes and bruises. But I was at the wire.

I had nothing to cut it with, so I had to burrow under it. Sounds easier than it actually is. A barb took a nick out of the back of my neck and I felt blood welling out of it while the salt sweat made it smart like fury. Then the coil caught in my shirt. I had to force myself to be slow, unhurried, when all I wanted to do was stand up and rip myself free of it frantically. Then it caught in my webbing, and finally in my trousers. I had to suppress an insane urge to laugh at the absurdity of it all. Finally I was through, feeling as though I had just run a marathon. I was whacked, but the adrenalin was keeping me going. I dashed into the shadow of a longhouse's stilts and crouched there in the deeper shadow trying to get my breathing under control.

The glimmerings of a plan had been coming to the surface while I watched the base that afternoon, and now I put it into action. I made a run for the sentry tower, waiting until the mindlessly bored sentry had turned the other way. Once underneath it I was invisible, though getting out from under it would be a different story. I unpacked the C4 and det cord and went to work. When I was finished, I got out my own parachute cord from my survival kit and lashed the flash initiator to a leg of the watch-tower. I still had thirty feet of para cord left, so I tied it to the trigger button on the initiator. One tug, and the sparks would fly.

I looked up, listening to the clumping of the sentry's feet on the platform of the tower above me. When they were headed towards the perimeter, I ran for it, wincing helplessly at the thought of a bullet in the back, and trailing the para cord after me into the shelter of another longhouse. It was just long enough, and I tied it to one of the longhouse's supporting stilts at knee height.

I had fishing line with me in the survival kit too, and with it I rigged up my two grenades, setting the line across the steps which came down from two of the noisiest longhouses. Then, and only then, did I finally make a beeline for the headquarters hut.

There was a light inside, and men talking. I could smell cigarette smoke and old, spicy food. The building had a kind of porch which creaked under my tread even though my footfalls were as light as a baby's fart.

Another smell, odd and unpleasant, like meat that's gone off. I caught only a whiff of it before the cigarette smoke hid it again. I stepped up to the door and peered in.

Chalky, strapped to a chair nude right in front of me. A stick was jammed between his teeth and secured with rope around the back of his head. Blood trickled from the corners of his mouth. His teeth were mashed, and there was something odd about the shape of his head which I couldn't fathom for a moment. He was conscious, and saw me straight away. His eyes widened slightly, but that was all.

Two more men, both with their backs to me. They held parangs which shone with blood. They'd been carving him up. They stood in a shimmery puddle of his blood, and bits of his flesh spattered their boots.

Ever seen anything like that? No, I'll bet you fucking haven't. Even if you've seen a fair bit of gore, it knocks you on your arse if it's the face of a friend you see staring out of that blood and filth.

I backed away from the door, and for a second I nearly lost it. A hammering red fury beat about my head. I was close to letting go of it, but managed to get a grip on myself. Slowly, I set down the SLR and drew my knife – a big, broad-bladed thing which could almost do service as a short sword.

I stood there a moment, remembering details from the interior, how the men stood, what was where. Then I stepped casually in the door.

One turned around in the act of putting a cigarette to his lips. He never got it there. My knife took him just above the collar-bone, slashed his jugular and severed his windpipe. He dropped to his knees, hands going to his throat, gargling.

The other had backed away a step and was

shouting something and raising his parang at the same time. I stepped forward. One hand gripped his wrist, immobilizing the parang. The other drove the knife into his eye with all the strength I had in me. I felt the blade grate on the bone of the socket, and jammed it right into the hilt. The man dropped like a stone as it pierced his brain, crashing to the floor and upsetting a rickety table.

Noise outside which I was barely aware of. There was a kind of red haze in my mind, but I felt clear-headed, logical. I retrieved the SLR and saw that men were moving outside, shouting. The commotion within the hut had not gone unnoticed. I went back inside, ground the knife out of the corpse it impaled and cut Chalky free of his bonds. He fell forward. The smell was clear and strong now. They'd cut him up badly, lacerating his legs and lower torso. An ear was gone. And gangrene was already in the wounds, maggots crawling in his flesh.

'Can't, Jock. No good . . .' he mumbled.

I whipped the SLR into my shoulder and fired at the man coming into the door. Three rounds blew him back out again. Then I bent and got Chalky in a fireman's lift, hoisting him over my shoulder, rifle in one hand. A burst of gunfire came through the iron walls of the hut. I went out through the back. A shape running in the darkness. All kinds of yelling and commotion now. I shot a man who seemed barely aware of us – two rounds from the hip which opened out his belly and blasted from his spine. He went down soundlessly. Then I ran, Chalky light as a feather on my shoulder, and got under a longhouse. I set him down there, and began feeding the tracer rounds which I had taped to my rifle into the top of my magazine.

Four sharp, short explosions, softer and flatter than rifle fire. The watch-tower of the base tilted at a crazy angle and came crashing down. I'd set charges on all four of his legs. Someone must have run into the para cord.

The crump of a grenade, and a few seconds later another. Men were screaming now. Wild gunfire rattled out into the night, tracer careered up into the air. My little devices were sowing a spot of confusion.

I turned to Chalky. 'You can't walk, mate.'

He shook his head. 'I'm fucked, Jock. You mad fucking Scot. You glorious nutter.'

'That's me,' I said, and sighted on the drums of petrol by the MT yard. I fired two rounds at them, and they went up, the phosphorus on the tracer rounds igniting the stuff and lighting up the night with a huge fireball. One of the trucks was blasted on to its side and lay there burning.

'Mad as a fucking hatter,' I said calmly. I wiped the tears out of my eyes and sighted on the drums down by the jetty. Three more tracer rounds, and then they went up too. The jetty exploded into a million splinters of shattered wood. Burning fragments of it fell on the roofs of the other longhouses. Men were still running around firing at shadows. I killed one who came too close – two rounds to the throat and head from a bare twenty yards.

'It's no good, is it, Chalky?' I said, my throat hoarse and raw.

He shook his head tiredly. 'No, Jock. Nice gesture, though. Time you were out of here now. Just finish it off and get going.'

I remembered Malaya, when I had thought I was going to die. I remembered a dozen drunken evenings, a hundred madcap episodes. Chalky at my elbow for damn near all of them.

'Do it, Jock.'

He closed his eyes when I put the muzzle of the SLR to his temple. When it was done I stood up, feeling more alone than I ever had before. Then I started out at a run, leapt the perimeter wire like a deer, with bullets cracking bark off the trees above me, and kept going.

Postscript

The conflict in Borneo finally came to an end on 11 August 1966, bringing victory for British forces and aims in the region. As a result, Malaysia would remain independent of Indonesia, and free of Communist interference. For such a 'low-intensity' conflict, the casualties were fairly high. One hundred and fourteen British troops killed, 181 wounded. Five hundred and ninety Indonesian troops killed, 222 wounded and 771 captured. The tally of casualties does not include Malaysian civilians or a large number of 'unofficial' Indonesian dead whose bodies were never accounted for.

The Haunted House, where the SAS had their headquarters, still exists in Brunei. It is still haunted, and the local people continue to avoid it.

OTHER TITLES IN SERIES FROM 22 BOOKS

Available now at newsagents and booksellers
or use the order form provided

continued overleaf . . .

ECHO THREE ZERO

All at £4.99

All 22 Books are available at your bookshop, or can be ordered from:

22 Books
Cash Sales Department
P.O. Box 11
Falmouth
Cornwall
TR10 9EN
Tel: +44 (0) 1326 372400
Fax: +44 (0) 1326 374888
Email: books@barni.avel.co.uk.

POST AND PACKING:
Payments can be made as follows: cheque or postal order, payabl⁻
to Little, Brown and Company (UK) or by credit cards. Do not
send cash or currency.

While every effort is made to keep prices low it is sometimes
necessary to increase cover prices at short notice. 22 Books
reserves the right to show new retail prices on covers which may
differ from those previously advertised in the books or elsewhere.

NAME ....

ADDRESS ....

....

POST/ZIP CODE ....

☐ Please keep me in touch with future 22 Books publications
☐ I enclose my remittance for £ _____
☐ I wish to pay by Visa/Access/Mastercard/Eurocard

Card number

☐☐☐☐ ☐☐☐☐ ☐☐☐☐ ☐☐☐☐

Card expiry date

☐☐ ☐☐

Please allow 28 days for delivery. Please tick box if you do not
wish to receive any additional information ☐